Benedetti, Mario, comp.
Unstill life; an introduction to the Spanish poetry of Latin America
Harcourt, 1969
127 p illus

English and Spanish

1. Spanish American poetry- 20th cent.
I. Title

UNSTILL LIFE | NATURALEZA VIVA

Introducción a la Poesía Hispanoamericana

NATURALEZA VIVA

Editada por
MARIO BENEDETTI

Traducción de
DARWIN J. FLAKOLL Y CLARIBEL ALEGRÍA

Ilustraciones de
ANTONIO FRASCONI

Harcourt, Brace & World, Inc., New York

An Introduction to the Spanish Poetry of Latin America

UNSTILL LIFE

Edited by
MARIO BENEDETTI

Translated by
DARWIN J. FLAKOLL AND CLARIBEL ALEGRÍA

Illustrated by
ANTONIO FRASCONI

Harcourt, Brace & World, Inc., New York

Library of Congress Catalog Card Number: 69-17114
Printed in the United States of America
FIRST EDITION

The editor wishes to thank the authors and publishers who have given their permission to reprint the poems in this collection, which were taken from the following sources:

JORGE ENRIQUE ADOUM, *Antología de la poesía viva latinoamericana*, edited by Aldo Pellegrini, Editorial Seix Barral S.A., Barcelona, 1966.

CLARIBEL ALEGRÍA, *Vía única*, Editorial Alfa, Montevideo, 1965.

CARLOS GERMÁN BELLI, *El pie sobre el cuello*, Colección Carabela, Editorial Alfa, Montevideo, 1967.

ERNESTO CARDENAL, *Oración por Marilyn Monroe y otros poemas*, Ediciones La Tertulia, Medellín, 1965.

JUAN CUNHA, *Triple tentativa*, Ediciones Número, Montevideo, 1954.

RUBÉN DARÍO, *Cantos de vida y esperanza*, Tipografía de la Revista de Archivos, Bibliotecas y Museos, Madrid, 1905.

JUAN GELMAN, *Gotán*, Colección de poesía La Rosa Blindada, Ediciones Horizonte, Buenos Aires, 1962.

NICOLÁS GUILLÉN, *Antología mayor*, Ediciones Unión, Havana, 1964.

VICENTE HUIDOBRO, *Obras completas*, Editora Zig-Zag, Santiago, Chile, 1964.

JUANA DE IBARBOUROU, *El cántaro fresco*, Ed. Maximino García, Montevideo, 1920.

GABRIELA MISTRAL, *Antología*, Editora Zig-Zag, Santiago, Chile, 1941.

MARCO ANTONIO MONTES DE OCA, *Fundación del entusiasmo*, Universidad Nacional Autónoma de México, México, 1963.

BALDOMERO FERNÁNDEZ MORENO, *Antología 1915-1940*, Colección Austral, Ed. Espasa-Calpe Argentina S.A., Buenos Aires, 1941.

PABLO NERUDA, *Obras completas*, Editorial Losada S.A., Buenos Aires,1956.

NICANOR PARRA, *Poemas y antipoemas*, Editorial Nascimento, Santiago, Chile, 1954.

JOAQUIN PASOS, *Poemas de un joven*, Colección Tezontle, Fondo de Cultura Económica, México, 1962.

OCTAVIO PAZ, *Libertad bajo palabra, obra poética (1935-1958)*, Colección Letras Mexicanas, Fondo de Cultura Económica, México, 1960.

ROBERTO FERNÁNDEZ RETAMAR, *Poesía reunida*, Ediciones Unión, Havana, 1966.

JAIME SABINES, *Casa de las Américas*, No. 30, May-June 1965, Havana.

SEBASTIÁN SALAZAR BONDY, *El tacto de la araña*, Francisco Moncloa Editores S.A., Lima, 1966.

ALFONSINA STORNI, *Antología poética*, Collección Austral, Ed. Espasa-Calpe Argentina S.A., Buenos Aires, 1940.

CÉSAR VALLEJO, *Poesías completas*, Editorial Losada S.A., Buenos Aires, 1949.

IDEA VILARIÑO, *Nocturnos*, Ediciones Número, Montevideo, 1955.

CONTENTS

Contents

INTRODUCTION

Latin-American literature, developing at a time when other cultures had already acquired wisdom and experience through many generations, found itself disoriented from the very beginning. Confronted with a wealth of European models, it was deprived of the opportunity to undergo an innocent, spontaneous growth. Having arrived tardily at the art game, one of its main preoccupations from the early colonial era to the present day has been to bring itself up to date.

Nonetheless, one of the legitimate attractions of this literature has been its very backwardness. Some of the healthy passion of Sarmiento, the Argentine educator and man of affairs, still reaches us across the years from 1842 when he defended—against Andres Bello's attacks—a Romanticism that Sarmiento admitted in advance was already dead and buried in Europe. He was conscious that, even though European literature had fulfilled and gone beyond this Romanticism, the new continent had yet to comprehend and appropriate it, since it coincided more closely with the anxieties of Latin America's unfinished political revolution than did the rigid academicism of the Classicists.

On one occasion only did Latin America pull ahead of the Old World's advances. Paradoxically, this overtaking was provoked by its many accumulated arrears. A period occurred (from 1870 to 1890, approximately) in which Latin-American writers found that they held in their hands a Classicism that they had copiously imitated but had not re-created; a Romanticism, equally imitated, which seemed to them uncomfortable and inflated; and in addition, a stammering native style, whose backwardness had nothing to do with Europe but everything to do with the urgent, postponed reality in Latin America.

From these three inadequacies stemmed a single advance. As Arturo Torres-Ríoseco, the Chilean critic, has pointed out, "The Hispano-Americans were sure that it was something new, something very modern, and for lack of a more clearly defined name," they gave it "the name of Modernism." Modernism has Classical, Romantic, and native elements; it has Spanish, French, English, and other overtones. But inasmuch as these are blended together, it is for that very reason typically Latin-American, since the Modernists were the first to see that the only rootedness possible in this region of crisscrossed racial and cultural paths lay in accentuating their very rootlessness.

Typical of the Modernists is Rubén Darío, the Nicaraguan poet. As his compatriot, Ernesto Cardenal, tells us, "Rubén Darío was born in a land of transit, and, symbolically, his mother gave birth to him in mid-journey aboard a cart that was passing through Metapa." The detail of the cart is picturesque—who can deny it?—and might lend itself to a good many easy allegories, but I prefer to pause before that other detail of "mid-journey." It occurs to me that Darío's poetry was born the same way, in the midst of a long journey that set out from Victor Hugo, the Frenchman, and has arrived today at Pablo Neruda, the Chilean. I have no doubt that the itinerary of Latin-American poetry would be very different had it not been for that decisive and illuminating stopover in Metapa.

There is in Darío one poet who looks back on the past and another who demands a future; one who attacks the United States and another who flatters Uncle Sam; one who poses quasi-political questions to the swan and another who bids the owl to guard his perennial silence; one who uses and abuses voluptuousness as a style and system and another who recovers his infancy in one of the most stark and sober evocations (*Allá lejos*) that poetry has ever presented; one who in 1901 enthusiastically enrolls in the ancient tradition of sinfulness (*Que el amor no admite cuerdas reflexiones*) and another who in the year of his death repents and turns remorseful (*Salmo*) in a desperate tug-of-war with his memories of temptation.

Darío, this "madman of twilights and dawns," was undoubtedly in advance of his time. A good part of the best Spanish poetry written and published in the past twenty years stems from him in a way that is not forced but natural. Today one can speak of his *Canto a la Argentina* as a preliminary draft of Neruda's *Canto general.* And there are other omens. Some studies of Darío commence by affirming that Modernism is dead, and from this affirmation they deduce forcefully that Darío's poetry is equally dead. Because of this, it seems opportune to point out here that in Darío's work there are many poems (and not always those written in his last years) that stand outside the widest possible definitions of Modernism. Singularly enough, these fugitive pieces are the ones that seem to be most clearly modern. Poems such as the already mentioned *Allá lejos* or those that make up the series, *A Francisca,* foreshadow an entire current of present-day poetry, which is intimate, frank, tender, and at the same time stark. The *Epístola a la señora de Leopoldo Lugones* is so contemporary that it may be read as if it had been written last week, without having to make a prior historical displacement of one's spirit. Octavio Paz, the Mexican poet, categorizes this poem as "an undoubted antecedent of what would become one of the conquests of contemporary poetry; the fusion between literary language and the language of the city." It must be added that this entire concept of what has come to be known as "prosaic poetry"—a flourishing mode among today's Latin-American poets—is prefigured in Darío's poem written in 1907.

Nevertheless, it must be recognized that Darío (though he is still enjoyable, still artistically alive, still prodigiously contemporary in various of his discoveries) signifies the past. Today it seems very clear that in contemporary Hispano-American poetry, the two great figures are Pablo Neruda, of Chile, and César Vallejo, of Peru. I do not propose to become mired in deciding which is the worthiest: whether the incessant, overwhelming torrent of the Chilean, or the dry, sometimes uneven, visceral, and explosive language of the Peruvian, vital to the point of suffering. I believe that it is possible to underscore an essential difference between the influences which the one and the other has exercised and continues to exercise on the succeeding generations that inevitably recognize their mastery.

Whereas Neruda has exerted a more or less paralyzing influence, as if the richness of his verbal torrent permits only an imitation, Vallejo, in contrast, has established himself as the motive force and stimulus of the most authentically creative Latin-American poets of the present day. Not in vain does the work of Nicanor Parra, Sebastián Salazar Bondy, Gonzalo Rojas, Ernesto Cardenal, Roberto Fernández Retamar, and Juan Gelman reveal, either directly or through mediating influences, the Vallejo trademark; not in vain does each of these have, despite this common bond, an unmistakable voice of his own. To this list one would have to add other names—Idea Vilariño, Pablo Armando Fernández, Enrique Lihn, Claribel Alegría, Humberto Megget, and Joaquin Pasos—that, situated at a greater distance from Vallejo than those previously mentioned, are still closer in poetic attitude to Vallejo, the author of

Poemas humanos, than to Neruda, the author of *Residencia en la tierra.*

It is difficult to find a likely explanation of this undeniable fact. I should like to risk a personal interpretation of the above-mentioned phenomenon. Neruda's poetry is, above all, words. Few works have been or will be written in Spanish with so astonishing a verbal luxuriousness as the first two volumes of *Residencia en la tierra* or certain passages of the *Canto general.* There is no one like Neruda for achieving an unusual poetical sparkle simply by coupling a noun and an adjective that have never before been placed in proximity to one another. Of course, there is also in Neruda's work sensitivity, attitudes, commitment, emotion, but (even when the poet doesn't always want it that way) everything seems to be placed at the noble service of his words. Human sensitivity, wide though it may be, passes almost unnoticed in his poetry when compared with his sensitivity to language; political attitudes and commitments, however explosive they appear, give way in importance to the artistic attitude and commitment that the poet assumes before each word, before each of his agreements and disagreements.

Neruda's use of metaphors has such power that, through innumerable acolytes or followers, it reappears like an ineffaceable, inextinguishable gene. Vallejo's legacy, in contrast, reaches its addressees by other paths and by touching, perhaps, other hidden springs. Never, even in his best moments, does the Peruvian's poetry give the impression of torrential spontaneity. It is evident that Vallejo struggles resolutely with language, and frequently when he finally manages to subdue the indomitable word, he cannot prevent the scars of the combat from showing. If Neruda takes possession of the word gently and with its full consent, Vallejo, in contrast, violates it, making it accept and express by main force a new and unusual meaning. Neruda surrounds the word with unaccustomed neighbors but without distorting its essential significance; Vallejo, on the other hand, obliges the word to be and to say something that did not previously figure in its strict meaning. Neruda bypasses the dictionary only infrequently; Vallejo, in contrast, continually contradicts it. The combat that Vallejo unleashes against the word displays the strange harmony of his anarchic, dissenting character but does not necessarily lead to a literary harmony in the orthodox sense. It is as a human spectacle (and not only as a purely artistic exercise) that Vallejo's poetry fascinates his reader, and once this first astonishment is kindled, all the rest becomes something subsidiary, however worthwhile it may be as an intermediary agent.

When poet-readers, that is those poets influenced by Vallejo, recognize that this language is a necessity, not a luxury, they do not stop there, bedazzled. Since each poem is a battlefield, they must go further, seek the human background, encounter the man, and then support his attitude, participate in his emotion, assist him in his commitment, suffer with his suffering. For Neruda's poet-readers, he functions above all as a literary model. Vallejo by means of his poems serves as a human model. I would not dare assert that Vallejo's work is the most perfect achievement that Hispano-American poetry has attained, but I am sure that it is the poetry which most profoundly transmits the Latin-American condition, the suffocating contradictions of certain absurdities that occur only in our countries, the tremendous confusion that compassion and rage produce when they meet or clash within the same sensitive vision. It may be said that in Latin America no one has written better human poems (and one of his books is entitled, precisely, *Poemas humanos*) than César Vallejo.

Before turning to other matters, I would like, in passing, to touch on the theme of commitment, even though, for obvious reasons, it is not always recognizable in the material presented here. More than once in Latin America harsh criticisms have been raised against the writer who refuses to commit himself, who avoids squaring his acts with the dictates of his conscience. It is worth noting that this is a key theme for the Latin-American writer. Naturally, we are no longer talking of that pure, uncontaminated conscience that for centuries was the ethical catechizer of Western civilization. No, today the conscience of a human being is contaminated by the conscience of his neighbor. Arthur Miller once pointed out that "man is inside society, and society is inside man," and this is particularly valid in Latin America. That is to say that society is also inside conscience, and therefore conscience can no longer avoid social conditioners. The small (and valid) social conscience of the individual, and by extension that of the poet, is integrated into the great social conscience of his class, of his nation, and, expanding the term to its widest limits, of all Latin America as well.

It is not my intention to consider in detail here the work of each of the authors included in this book. In any case, next to each poem there appears a bio-bibliographical note in which the reader may find the most significant facts about each artist. If I have treated the outstanding figures of Darío, Neruda, and Vallejo with certain care, it is simply because with these three names Latin-American poetry attains an exceptional level of quality: a level which, if we take into account more recent production, it seems determined to maintain.

Finally, in order to avoid any possible misunderstanding, I wish to make clear that this selection of poems is not a true anthology of Hispano-American poetry, since it contains only twenty-three examples. It is only an introduction. It was decided to choose as a starting point the figure of Darío (whose hundredth anniversary was recently celebrated) and the use of this key date, 1867, necessarily excluded from the volume earlier poets. One may think of Sor Juana Inés de la Cruz, Bartolomé Hidalgo, José Hernández, González Prada, Martí, Julián del Casal, José Asunción Silva, to mention only some of the great figures of Hispano-American poetry who were born before Darío. Since some of the best contemporary poets do not always deal with themes that might interest young people, we have omitted such important writers as Delmira Agustini, Jaimes Freyre, and the more recent Gonzalo Rojas, José Emilio Pacheco, Enrique Lihn, Pablo Armando Fernández. It was also necessary to set aside estimable poets (Leopoldo Lugones, Herrera y Reissig) who, owing to the particular and strict use they make of rhyme and rhythm, lose enormously when they are translated into other languages.

These twenty-three poems are no more than a partial sample of Hispano-American poetry. I am confident, however, that young North American readers will discover in perusing them elements sufficiently attractive that they will seek new and wider contacts with the excellent poetry that is being lived and written, enjoyed and suffered, in that vast, disquieting region to the south of the Rio Grande, which is struggling to become conscious of its destiny and attempting by all possible means to obtain its second and true independence.

MARIO BENEDETTI

UNSTILL LIFE | NATURALEZA VIVA

RUBÉN DARÍO

Nicaragua (1867-1916)

The great Nicaraguan poet was born in Metapa January 18, 1867. Thereafter, Darío's nonliterary biography can be condensed into a few references: two marriages, one by free choice (with Rafaela Contreras) and the other stemming from violent pressure (with Rosario Murillo); a certain lasting, though unofficial, union (with Francisca Sanchez); various diplomatic positions (representing Colombia and Nicaragua) and newspaper jobs (the most important as correspondent for *La Nación* of Buenos Aires); constant travel, much alcohol, frequent political concessions and isolated gestures of civic valor; a spendthrift style of life, serious economic anguish, death in Nicaragua on February 6, 1916, beside the invincible Rosario; a postmortem scandal during which family members and friends, revolvers in hand, disputed possession of the poet's heart and brain. His most important books of poetry are: *Prosas profanas y otros poemas*, 1896; *Cantos de vida y esperanza*, 1905; *El canto errante*, 1907; *Poema del otoño y otros poemas*, 1910.

It is perhaps impossible to understand and explain this towering poet if one fails to comprehend that, despite his powerful verbal torrent and his exceptional dominion over verse, he was also a weak, disconcerted person, childishly gluttonous for the economic stability he never attained, and, above all, essentially solitary. His eroticism (who *is*, who is not erotic?), which has been so carefully sifted by critics and biographers, is something more than a leitmotiv and sallies forth from his work to daringly confront death. The frivolous playfulness of his first weak poems is converted in *Prosas profanas* into a mature, calculated elegance; this gives way to existential anguish in which the poet participates, a badly wounded witness, in the condemnation of love, the hecatomb of the senses, the extortion and blackmail of death. He is a man of little faith, but ever hopeful it will increase; his style of life is atheistic, certainly, but always with the hope that he will be purified. Darío himself, through Chiron in the *Coloquio de los centauros*, justifies this harmony of dissident elements: "The dove and the crow are forms of the Enigma."

Letanía de nuestro señor Don Quijote

Rey de los hidalgos, señor de los tristes,
que de fuerza alientas y de ensueños vistes,
coronado de áureo yelmo de ilusión;
que nadie ha podido vencer todavía,
por la adarga al brazo, toda fantasía,
y la lanza en ristre, toda corazón.

Noble peregrino de los peregrinos,
que santificaste todos los caminos
con el paso augusto de tu heroicidad,
contra las certezas, contra las conciencias
y contra las leyes y contra las ciencias,
contra la mentira, contra la verdad . . .

Caballero errante de los caballeros,
barón de varones, príncipe de fieros,
par entre los pares, maestro, ¡salud!
¡Salud, porque juzgo que hoy muy poca tienes
entre los aplausos o entre los desdenes,
y entre las coronas y los parabienes
y las tonterías de la multitud!

¡Tú, para quien pocas fueron las victorias
antiguas, y para quien clásicas glorias
serían apenas de ley y razón,
soportas elogios, memorias, discursos,
resistes certámenes, tarjetas, concursos,
y, teniendo a Orfeo, tienes a orfeón!

Litany of Our Sire, Don Quixote

King of all nobles, lord of the sad,
by virtue inspired, in daydreams clad,
crowned with an aureate, hallucinate helm;
the scutcheoned shield graven with romance
and pennoned spirit flutt'ring from your lance,
defend your invincible, vaporous realm.

Of all life's wayfarers, you, their patron saint,
by your stark, heroic passage swept a taint
from the world's highways; 'twas you who broke the pact
twixt certitude and arrogant conviction,
twixt law and scientistic predilection,
twixt falsehood and tyranny of fact.

Of all knight errants perhaps the most curious,
virility's viceroy, prince of the furious,
peer among peers, I drink to your health.
Your health, then! You must have little remaining
after all the applauding and all the disdaining,
the crownings and praisings waxing and waning,
and the stupidities of the commonwealth.

You, for whom victories few were and flitting,
for whom classic glories scarce would seem fitting,
could never have deemed that your triumph would be
to tolerate eulogies, memorials, critics' disquisitions,
endure polemics, graven tablets, literary competitions,
and, with Orpheus' ear, be forced to hear
choral groups singing off-key.

Escucha, divino Rolando del sueño,
a un enamorado de tu Clavileño,
y cuyo Pegaso relincha hacia ti;
escucha los versos de estas letanías,
hechas con las cosas de todos los días
y con otras que en lo misterioso vi.

¡Ruega por nosotros, hambrientos de vida,
con el alma a tientas, con la fe perdida,
llenos de congojas y faltos de sol,
por advenedizas almas de manga ancha,
que ridiculizan el ser de la Mancha,
el ser generoso y el ser español!

¡Ruega por nosotros, que necesitamos
las mágicas rosas, los sublimes ramos
de laurel! Pro nobis ora, gran señor.
(Tiemblan las florestas de laurel del mundo,
y antes que tu hermano vago, Segismundo,
el pálido Hamlet te ofrece una flor.)

Ruega generoso, piadoso, orgulloso;
ruega casto, puro, celeste, animoso;
por nos intercede, suplica por nos,
pues casi ya estamos sin savia, sin brote,
sin alma, sin vida, sin luz, sin Quijote,
sin pies y sin alas, sin Sancho y sin Dios.

De tantas tristezas, de dolores tantos,
de los superhombres de Nietzsche, de cantos
áfonos, recetas que firma un doctor,
de las epidemias, de horribles blasfemias
de las Academias,
¡líbranos, señor!

Listen, divine Roland of the winding horn,
to one enamoured of your Clavileño; I must warn
that my own Pegasus' discordant brayings
shall burden you with one more supplication,
composed in part of cryptic inspiration,
but in far greater part of hackneyed sayings.

Pray for us with our hunger for life,
with our faith adrift, our souls in strife;
anguish assails us; we yearn for light;
we sicken when shallow parvenus blanch
or sneer with disdain at the man of La Manche:
that generous being, the true Spanish knight.

Pray for us who have a dire need
of magic roses, a sublime creed
of laurel wreaths. *Pro nobis ora* in this hour.
(Before you every living laurel trembles,
and while errant Sigismund dissembles,
the pale prince of Denmark offers you a flower.)

Pray generously, piously and proudly,
pray chastely, purely, celestially, loudly;
intercede for us; Divine Attention prod
for us who die without your antidote,
without soul or life or light or Quixote,
without feet or wings, or Sancho or God.

From so many sadnesses, from so many sorrows,
from Nietzsche's Supermen who threaten our tomorrows,
from prescriptions of doctors and from epidemics,
from the horrid blasphemies of the Academics,
free us, gentle sire.

De rudos malsines,
falsos paladines,
y espíritus finos y blandos y ruines,
del hampa que sacia
su canallocracia
con burlar la gloria, la vida, el honor,
del puñal con gracia,
¡líbranos, señor!

Noble peregrino de los peregrinos,
que santificaste todos los caminos
con el paso augusto de tu heroicidad,
contra las certezas, contra las conciencias
y contra las leyes y contra las ciencias,
contra la mentira, contra la verdad . . .

Ora por nosotros, señor de los tristes,
que de fuerza alientas y de sueños vistes,
coronado de áureo yelmo de ilusión;
que nadie ha podido vencer todavía,
por la adarga al brazo, toda fantasía,
y la lanza en ristre, toda corazón!

From crude calumniators
and all false gladiators,
from those bland spirits of infamous story,
from every mobocracy
that apes aristocracy,
sneering at life, honor and glory,
and from the deft dagger stroke,
free us, gentle sire.

Of all life's wayfarers, you, their patron saint
by your stark, heroic passage swept a taint
from the world's highways; 'twas you who broke the pact
twixt certitude and arrogant conviction,
twixt law and scientistic predilection,
twixt falsehood and tyranny of fact.

Pray for us, lord of the sad,
by virtue inspired, in daydreams clad,
crowned with an aureate, hallucinate helm;
the scutcheoned shield graven with romance
and pennoned spirit flutt'ring from your lance,
defend your invincible, vaporous realm.

BALDOMERO FERNÁNDEZ MORENO

Argentina (1886-1950)

Moreno was born in Buenos Aires, Argentina, in 1886 and died in 1950. His is one of the most legitimate and indestructible names in Argentine poetry. "His verses," writes Anderson-Imbert, the Argentinian critic, "are apparently elementary, but always complex. Simple, but not prosaic. Fernández Moreno is the poet who installs himself solidly in the place where he lives and opens his eyes to his surroundings, faithful to what he is as a man and to what things are when seen in their essences."

His case is one of exceptional adaptation between inspiration and instrument. It is interesting to note that the more simple his poems appear and the more ordinary their packaging, the less one is aware of clanging rhymes in his verses. Only Antonio Machado was his superior in the arduous task of convincing the reader that the word which ends a line has been placed there because of its function rather than because of its sound. His principal books of poetry are: *Ciudad,* 1917; *Versos de Negrita,* 1920; *El hogar en el campo,* 1923; *El hijo,* 1926; *La tertulia de los viernes* and *Epístola de un verano,* 1935; *Yo, médico; yo catedrático,* 1941.

Setenta balcones y ninguna flor

Setenta balcones hay en esta casa,
setenta balcones y ninguna flor . . .
¿A sus habitantes, Señor, qué les pasa?
¿Odian el perfume, odian el color?

La piedra desnuda de tristeza agobia,
¡dan una tristeza los negros balcones!
¿No hay en esta casa una niña novia?
¿No hay algún poeta bobo de ilusiones?

¿Ninguno desea ver tras los cristales
una diminuta copia de jardín?
¿En la piedra blanca trepar los rosales,
en los hierros negros abrirse un jazmín?

Si no aman las plantas no amarán el ave,
no sabrán de música, de rimas, de amor.
Nunca se oirá un beso, jamás se oirá un clave . . .
¡Setenta balcones y ninguna flor!

Seventy Balconies and Not a Single Flower

There are seventy balconies in that house,
seventy balconies and not a single flower . . .
All its inhabitants, Lord, what's the matter?
Do they hate perfume? Do they hate bright color?

Naked stone overwhelms you with its sadness;
the black balconies infuse you with their gloom.
Doesn't a single love-struck girl reside there?
Not one poet demented by illusions?

Doesn't someone want to see through his windows
a diminutive copy of a garden?
See roses climbing up along the white stone,
a jasmine blooming against the black iron?

If they don't love plants, they would never love birds;
they'll know nothing of music, rhyming, or love.
They'll never hear a kiss or a piano.
Seventy balconies and not a single flower!

GABRIELA MISTRAL

Chile (1889-1957)

Her true name is Lucila Godoy Alcayaga. She was born in Vicuña, Chile, in 1889 and died in Hempstead, New York, in 1957. She was a rural teacher, school principal, and, finally, consul of her country in Italy, Spain, Portugal, Brazil, and the United States. In 1945 she received the Nobel Prize for literature.

As emphasized by the titles of her first books, Gabriela Mistral traveled from desolation to tenderness without forcing the transition or abandoning the sincerity that remains one of her cardinal merits. Despite the dexterity with which she manipulates her images, despite her intent to cloak herself within them, Gabriela Mistral's poetry will remain as denuded as the earth and salt and living God of which she sings. She does not believe she has the strength, nor does she wish for the strength, to hide her solitude, and in a harshly Christian manner she imposes on herself the sacrifice of displaying it.

Her poetic works are: *Desolación*, 1922; *Ternura*, 1924; *Tala*, 1938; *Lagar*, 1954.

Balada

El pasó con otra;
yo le vi pasar.
Siempre dulce el viento
y el camino en paz.
¡Y estos ojos míseros
le vieron pasar!

El va amando a otra
por la tierra en flor.
Ha abierto el espino;
pasa una canción.
¡Y él va amando a otra
por la tierra en flor!

El besó a la otra
a orillas del mar;
resbaló en las olas
la luna de azahar.
¡Y no untó mi sangre
la extensión del mar!

El irá con otra
por la eternidad.
Habrá cielos dulces.
(Dios quiere callar)
¡Y él irá con otra
por la eternidad!

Ballad

He passed with another;
I watched him pass by.
The breeze stayed as sweet,
the road just as peaceful.
And these wretched eyes
watched him passing by!

He's loving another
o'er the flowering earth.
The hawthorn is blooming;
a melody drifts by.
And he's loving another
o'er the flowering earth!

He kissed the other
by the edge of the sea;
an orange blossom moon
stumbled in the waves.
The wide expanse of sea
couldn't assuage my heart!

He'll go with another
throughout eternity.
The skies will remain sweet
(God will remain silent).
and he'll go with another
throughout eternity!

ALFONSINA STORNI

Argentina (1892-1938)

This Argentine writer, the daughter of Swiss parents, was born in 1892 in Sala Capriasca, Cantón Tesino, Switzerland. She resided in Argentina from an early age. In 1910 she received her degree as a rural teacher, and she subsequently taught in Rosario and in Buenos Aires. Aware that she had cancer, she committed suicide in Mar del Plata on October 25, 1938.

Apparently, Alfonsina Storni's theme is man—or woman—with no other complications. But, strictly speaking, she deals with the man or woman of the city. The city in her work has a phantasmal presence: it is a jungle of houses, "some beside others, some behind others, some above others, some before others," and beneath it the other jungle—the human jungle—moves, "but not in a straight line." The bitter, hostile city arises to impede reciprocal communication between men, and everything remains half done, everything is left unfinished: language, love, hope, and even Alfonsina's own life, which she preferred to frustrate by tossing it into the sea.

Her principal books of poetry are: *El dulce daño*, 1918; *Irremediablemente*, 1919; *Languidez*, 1920; *Mundo de siete pozos*, 1924; *Ocre*, 1925; *Mascarilla y trébol*, 1938.

El adolescente del osito

En la penumbra de la salita
las lámparas
abrían su luz velada
de estrellas madrugantes.

Las espaldas femeninas
recogían la claridad
de los espejos.

Palabras
de puntas nocivas
buscaban
un corazón
no maduro.

Parado junto al piano,
el adolescente,
masa de luna
herida de ojos y boca,
sonreía.

Ojos expertos
se adelantaban en tanto
a la caza
vedada.

Mujer y hombre . . .
Mujer y hombre . . .
Mujer y hombre . . .

Adolescent with Bear

In the gloom of the living room
the lamps
disclosed their veiled light
of dawn-faded stars.

Feminine shoulders
gathered brightness
from the mirrors.

Poison-tipped words
sought out
an immature heart.

Standing beside the piano,
the adolescent,
a moon fragment
with wounds for eyes and mouth,
smiled.

Expert eyes
forged ahead meanwhile
in their illicit hunt.

Woman and man . . .
Woman and man . . .
Woman and man . . .

Crecía el cuchicheo
como los líquenes
en las selvas húmedas.

El adolescente solo,
acariciaba el osito
que adornaba el piano.

Sobre el pecho, ahora,
el osito amarillo
le hería, con la aspereza
de su lana,
los caminos abandonados
del corazón . . .

The whispering
spread like fungus
in damp jungles.

The lone adolescent
stroked the toy bear
adorning the piano.

Against his breast now,
the yellow bear
wounded, with wool's
roughness,
the abandoned pathways
of the heart.

CÉSAR VALLEJO

Peru (1892-1938)

The greatest poet of Peru and one of the greatest in Latin America was born in Santiago de Chuco on a date (between 1892 and 1895) that has remained in dispute between his biographers. After publication of his book *Trilce* (1922), he abandoned Peru and never returned. He maintained, in his poetry as well as in his life, a militant, committed attitude. He lived through the Civil War in Spain and testifies to that upheaval in *España, aparta de mí este cáliz.* He died in Paris on April 15, 1938. In one of his most famous poems, he had foreseen: "I will die in Paris when it's raining/on a day I already remember . . ."

Vallejo is—and it is thus that José Carlos Mariátegui, a Peruvian social essayist, distinguishes him—"acutely nostalgic. He has an evocative tenderness. But evocation in Vallejo is always subjective. One must not confuse the nostalgia which he conceives with such lyric purity with the literary nostalgia of worshippers of the past." In Vallejo there is a depth of honesty, of innocence, of sadness, of rebellion, of laceration, of something we might call fraternal solitude, and it is in this depth that one must seek the not always clear reasons for his undeniable influence on contemporary Latin-American poetry. In this Peruvian poet metaphors never prevent one from seeing life; rather, they are placed at the service of life. Vallejo, who fought desperately with words but drew out of his own depths an unexchangeable human quality, is miraculously confirmed in our present day.

His poetic works are: *Los heraldos negros,* 1918; *Trilce,* 1922; *Poemas humanos* (1923-1938), *España, aparta de mí este cáliz* (1937-1938).

La cólera que quiebra al hombre en niños

La cólera que quiebra al hombre en niños,
que quiebra al niño, en pájaros iguales,
y al pájaro, después, en huevecillos;
la cólera del pobre
tiene un aceite contra dos vinagres.

La cólera que al árbol quiebra en hojas,
a la hoja en botones desiguales
y al botón, en ranuras telescópicas;
la cólera del pobre
tiene dos ríos contra muchos mares.

La cólera que quiebra al bien en dudas,
a la duda, en tres arcos semejantes
y al arco, luego, en tumbas imprevistas;
la cólera del pobre
tiene un acero contra dos puñales.

La cólera que quiebra el alma en cuerpos,
al cuerpo en órganos desemejantes
y al órgano, en octavos pensamientos;
la cólera del pobre
tiene un fuego central contra dos cráteres.

The Rage That Shatters a Man into Children

The rage that shatters a man into children,
shatters the child into equivalent birds,
and the bird, then, into small round eggs;
the rage of the poor
has one part oil against two parts vinegar.

The rage that shatters a tree into leaves,
the leaf into unequal blossoms,
and the blossom into telescoped grooves;
the rage of the poor
has two rivers against many seas.

The rage that shatters goodness into doubting,
doubting into three equal arches,
and the arch, then, into unforeseen tombs;
the rage of the poor
has one steel against two daggers.

The rage that shatters a soul into bodies,
the body into dissimilar organs,
and the organ into eight thoughts;
the rage of the poor
has one central fire against two craters.

VICENTE HUIDOBRO

Chile (1893-1948)

The Chilean poet, the founder of Creationism, was born in Santiago in 1893 and died in 1948. He was a student of humanities, editor of literary reviews, candidate for presidency of the republic, a war correspondent. According to Huidobro himself, the term "Creationism" was coined in Buenos Aires as the result of a lecture the poet gave in the Argentine capital in 1916: "It was there they baptized me a Creationist for having said in my lecture that the first condition of a poet is to create, the second to create, the third to create."

Chilean literary critics frequently have been harsh with Huidobro. According to Raúl Silva Castro, he is an uneven writer, "more intellectual than inspired"; according to Arturo Torres-Ríoseco, he is a "third class poetic talent." Mariano Latorre, more generous, recognizes at least that the metaphor "is Huidobro's gift" and admits that his "humor is of good Chilean ancestry despite his French influences." The prestige that Huidobro's poetry presently enjoys among young Chilean poets and the invincible dynamism of his imagery demonstrate, twenty years after his death, that his genius had more strength than the soothsayers foretold.

Among his most outstanding poetic works are: *Adán*, 1916; *El espejo de agua*, 1916; *Horizon carré*, 1917; *Poemas árticos*, 1918; *Automne regulier*, 1925; *Tout a coup*, 1925; *Altazor*, 1931; *El ciudadano del olivido* (1924-1934), 1941.

Naturaleza viva

El deja al acordeón el fin del mundo
Paga con la lluvia la última canción
Allí donde las voces se juntan nace un enorme cedro
Más confortable que el cielo

Una golondrina me dice papá
Una anémona me dice mamá

Azul azul allí y en la boca del lobo
Azul Señor Cielo que se aleja
Qué dice usted Hacia dónde irá

Ah el hermoso brazo azul azul
Dad el brazo a la Señora Nube
Si tenéis miedo del lobo
El lobo de la boca azul azul
Del diente largo largo
Para devorar a la abuela naturaleza

Señor Cielo rasque su golondrina
Señora Nube apague sus anémonas

Las voces se juntan sobre el pájaro
Más grande que el árbol de la creación
Más hermoso que una corriente de aire entre dos astros

Unstill Life

He leaves the world's end to the accordion
Pays with rain for the last song
There where voices fuse an enormous cedar rises
More comforting than the sky

A swallow calls me papa
An anemone calls me mama

Blue blue there and in the mouth of the wolf
Blue Mister Sky who is leaving
What do you say Where is he going

Ah the beautiful blue blue arm
Offer your arm to Madame Cloud
If you are afraid of the wolf
The wolf with the blue blue mouth
and the long long teeth
To gobble up grandmother nature

Mister Sky scratch your swallow
Madame Cloud turn off your anemones

The voices mingle about the bird
Larger than the tree of creation
More beautiful than a current of air between two stars

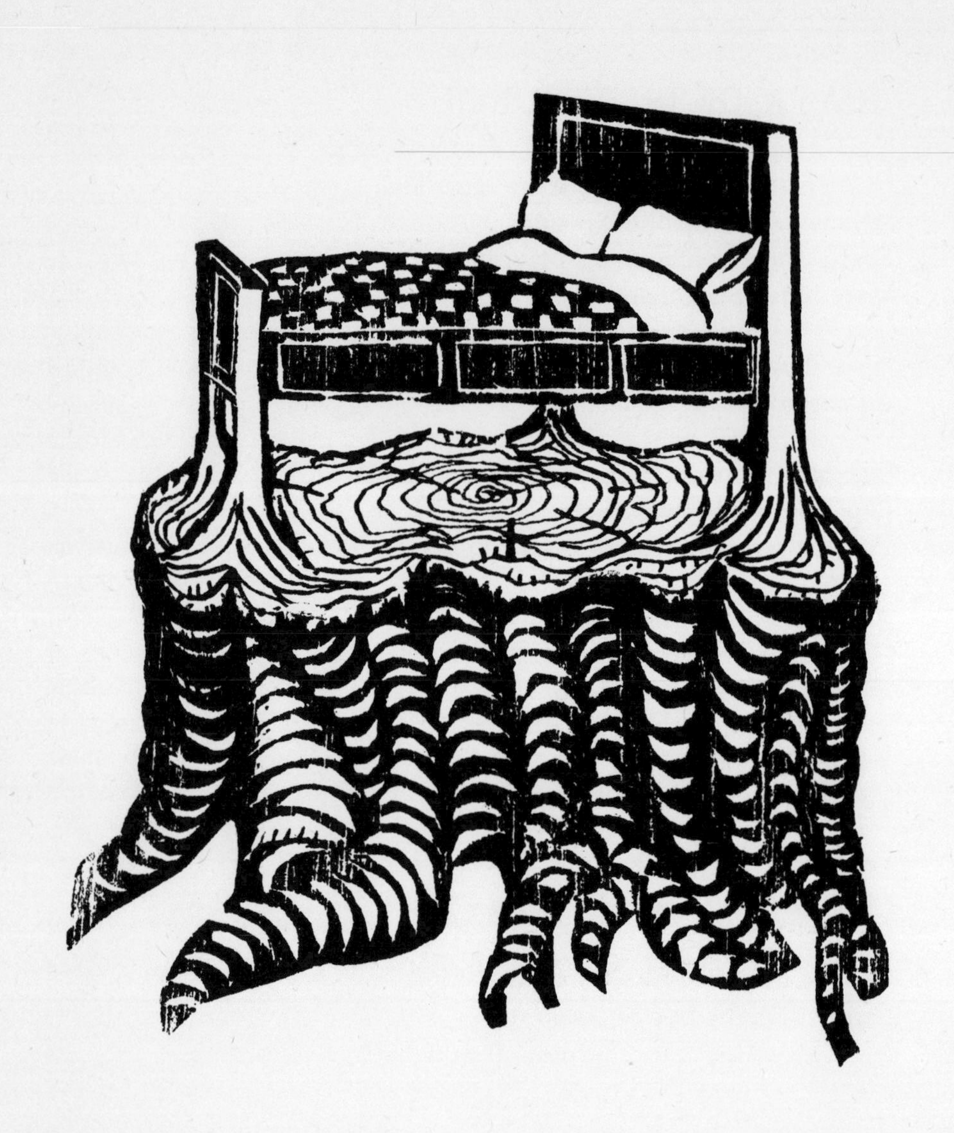

JUANA DE IBARBOUROU

Uruguay (1895-)

She has the greatest international renown of any feminine Uruguayan writer. She was born in 1895 in Melo, Cerro Largo. Her true name is Juana Fernández Morales, but with her first book, *Las lenguas de diamante* (1919), she adopted as a literary name the surname of her husband, Lucas Ibarbourou, a military man. In 1929, after she had published *El cántaro fresco* (1920) and *Raiz salvaje* (1922), a solemn ceremony was enacted in the Legislative Palace of Montevideo, during which she was consecrated as Juana of America. She is presently a member of the Uruguayan Academy of Letters.

"Juana de Ibarbourou's poetry," Alberto Zum Felde, the Uruguayan critic, has written, "is joy of life and plenitude of love. This pagan poetess in her first poems sings of the flavor of terrestrial life and of healthy, simple, instinctual love without psychological complications or moral sadness." Nevertheless, from her first jubilant and hedonistic books onward, this writer begins to glimpse the nightmare that is to come with solitude, deterioration, loss of beauty; it is precisely these themes that set the tone of her last books. "Her mystery," Gabriela Mistral, the well-known Chilean poetess, said of her, "is the most difficult of all: that of luminosity rather than shadows, and it would confound Dr. Faust himself."

Besides the books mentioned above, other titles that should be mentioned in her poetic work are: *La rosa de los vientos* (1930); *Perdida* (1950); and *Azor* (1953).

El nido

Mi cama fue un roble
y en sus ramas cantaban los pájaros,
mi cama fue un roble
y mordió la tormenta sus gajos.

Deslizo mis manos
por sus claros maderos pulidos,
y pienso que acaso toco el mismo tronco
donde estuvo aferrado algún nido.

Mi cama fue un roble.
Yo duermo en un árbol.
En un árbol amigo del agua,
del sol y la brisa, del cielo y del musgo,
de lagartos de ojuelos dorados
y de orugas de un verde esmeralda.

Yo duermo en un árbol.
¡Oh, amado, en un árbol dormimos!
Acaso por eso me parece el lecho,
esta noche, blando y hondo cual un nido.

Y en ti me acurruco como una avecilla
que busca el reparo de su compañero.
¡Que rezongue el viento, que gruña la lluvia!
Contigo en el nido, no sé lo que es miedo.

The Nest

My bed was an oak tree
and birds would sing in its branches,
my bed was an oak tree
and storms gnawed at its leaves.

I slide my hand along
its lustrous polished wood
and think I may touch the same trunk
to which a nest was bound.

My bed was an oak tree.
I slumber in a tree.
A tree that is friendly with rain,
sun, breezes, sky and moss,
lizards with little golden eyes,
emerald-green caterpillars.

I slumber in a tree.
Oh, my love, we sleep in a tree!
Perhaps that's why the bed tonight
seems as soft and deep as a nest.

I snuggle against you like a bird
seeking protection of its mate.
The wind may growl, the rain grumble!
Beside you in the nest, I'm not afraid.

NICOLÁS GUILLÉN

Cuba (1904-   )

This Cuban poet was born in Camagüey in 1904. He studied at the University of Havana and later devoted himself to journalism. Because of his militant political position, he was forced to live in exile for long periods (Mexico, Spain, France, the United States, Argentina, Uruguay, etc.). At present he resides in his own country, where he is president of the Union of Cuban Writers and Artists.

Guillén is probably the most outstanding cultivator of Negro poetry in Latin America. His work is combative, ironic, popular, anti-Yankee, but it is at the same time full of verbal invention, of an innate sense of rhythm, of a fine sensitivity for the human. After gaining an ample popularity in all of Latin America (Guillén is also a notable reciter of his own poems), he has inclined in recent years to a less direct style (for example, *El gran zoo*, the latest of his books), which is no less effective, thus demonstrating that he maintains intact his creative capacity and his spirit of renovation.

His poetic works are: *Motivos de son*, 1930; *Sóngora cosongo*, *West Indies, Ltd.*, 1934; *Cantos para soldados y sones para turistas*, 1937; *España*, 1937; *El son entero*, 1947; *La paloma de vuelo popular*, 1958; *El gran zoo*, 1967.

Balada de los dos abuelos

Sombras que sólo yo veo,
me escoltan mis dos abuelos.

Lanza con punta de hueso,
tambor de cuero y madera:
mi abuelo negro.
Gorguera en el cuello ancho,
gris armadura guerrera:
mi abuelo blanco.

Africa de selvas húmedas
y de gordos gongos sordos . . .
—¡Me muero!
(Dice mi abuelo negro).
Aguaprieta de caimanes,
verdes mañanas de cocos . . .
—¡Me canso!
(Dice mi abuelo blanco).
Oh velas de amargo viento,
galeón ardiendo en oro . . .
—¡Me muero!
(Dice mi abuelo negro).
¡Oh costas de cuello virgen
engañadas de abalorios . . .
—¡Me canso!
(Dice mi abuelo blanco).
¡Oh puro sol repujado,
preso en el aro del trópico;
oh luna redonda y limpia
sobre el sueño de los monos!

Ballad of the Two Grandfathers

Shades that I alone can see,
I walk with my two grandfathers.

A lance with a point of bone,
a drum of wood and leather:
my black grandfather.
About his wide neck a ruff,
in warrior's gray armor:
my white grandfather.

Africa's deep, damp jungles
and the dull, fat thud of drums . . .
"I'm dying!"
(Says my black grandfather).
Swamp water, alligators,
coconut green of morning . . .
"I'm weary!"
(Says my white grandfather).
Oh sails of the bitter breeze,
galleon blazing in gold . . .
"I'm dying!"
(Says my black grandfather).
Oh coasts whose virginal necks
were swindled with cheap glass beads . . .
"I'm weary!"
(Says my white grandfather).
Oh sun of pure hammered gold
held in the ring of tropic;
oh round, immaculate moon
above the dreams of monkeys!

¡Qué de barcos, qué de barcos!
¡Qué de negros, qué de negros!
¡Qué largo fulgor de cañas!
¡Qué látigo el del negrero!
Piedra de llanto y de sangre,
venas y ojos entreabiertos,
y madrugadas vacías,
y atardeceres de ingenio,
y una gran voz, fuerte voz
despedazando el silencio.
¡Qué de barcos, qué de barcos,
qué de negros!

Sombras que sólo yo veo,
me escoltan mis dos abuelos.

Don Federico me grita,
y Taita Facundo calla;
los dos en la noche sueñan,
y andan, andan.
Yo los junto.
—¡Federico!
¡Facundo! Los dos se abrazan.
Los dos suspiran. Los dos
las fuertes cabezas alzan;
los dos del mismo tamaño,
bajo las estrellas altas;
los dos del mismo tamaño,
ansia negra y ansia blanca,
los dos del mismo tamaño,
gritan, sueñan, lloran, cantan.
Sueñan, lloran, cantan.
Lloran, cantan.
¡Cantan!

How many! How many ships!
How many! How many blacks!
Sun blazing down on cane stalks!
The slave-driver's blacksnake whip!
A statue of tears and blood
and veins and half-closed eyes,
and all the empty mornings
and evenings at the mill,
and a great voice, a strong voice
tearing the silence to shreds.
How many! How many ships!
How many blacks!

Shades that I alone can see,
I walk with my two grandfathers.

Don Federico calls me;
Taita Facundo is quiet;
both in the night are dreaming
and walking, walking.
I bring them together.
Federico!
Facundo!
The two embrace, they sigh.
The two of them raise their heads;
the two of equal stature
beneath the vertex of stars;
the two of equal stature,
black anguish and white anguish;
the two of equal stature.
They shout, they dream, they weep, they sing.
They dream, they weep, they sing.
They weep, they sing.
They sing!

PABLO NERUDA

Chile (1904-   )

He is, without doubt, Latin America's greatest living poet. He was born in 1904 in Parral, Chile. His true name is Ricardo Neftalí Reyes Basoalto, but since the age of sixteen he has used the pseudonym of Pablo Neruda. He has been a consul and a senator. In 1945 he affiliated with the Communist party in Chile. In 1957 he became president of the Chilean Society of Writers. On various occasions he has figured among other candidates for the Nobel Prize for literature.

It is difficult to know what is the most creative element in his widely published *Veinte poemas de amor y una canción desesperada:* whether it be the different faces of love that serve as his context or his formidable capacity to find an original language destined to sing of this love. It is clear that while Neruda decidedly cultivates the sentimental (according to Amado Alonso, the Spanish critic and poet, "he introduces in the new schools a scandalous motive with his shameless cultivation of the heart"), it is only fair to note that he transcends mere sentimentality thanks to his unique use of images and his tireless bombardment with metaphors. The landscape comes to Neruda with love, is transfigured in his poetry by love; then this love becomes nature and, like it, overflows or defends its tranquillities.

Neruda also formulates a *poetic art,* though it is not necessary for him, as it was for Huidobro, to create *around* the object ("when the eyes look, it is created"). The truth, the wind, the nights demand of him his prophetic gift, and this constant birth of prophecies, this confused borning of images and words, is the element which produces that earnest impression of nostalgia and melancholy that Neruda always brings with him when he comes face to face with reality.

The principal titles of his poetic work are: *Veinte poemas de amor y una canción desesperada,* 1924; *Residencia en la tierra,* 2 volumes, 1935; *Tercera residencia,* 1947; *Canto general,* 1950; *Odas elementales,* 1954; *Neuevas odas elementales,* 1956; *Tercer libro de las odas,* 1957; *Extravagario,* 1958; *Canción de gesta,* 1960; *Plenos poderes,* 1962.

Poema 20

Puedo escribir los versos más tristes esta noche.

Escribir, por ejemplo: "La noche está estrellada,
y tiritan, azules, los astros, a lo lejos".

El viento de la noche gira en el cielo y canta.

Puedo escribir los versos más tristes esta noche.
Yo la quise, y a veces ella también me quiso.

En las noches como ésta la tuve entre mis brazos.
La besé tantas veces bajo el cielo infinito.

Ella me quiso, a veces yo también la quería.
Cómo no haber amado sus grandes ojos fijos.

Puedo escribir los versos más tristes esta noche.
Pensar que no la tengo. Sentir que la he perdido.

Oír la noche inmensa, más inmensa sin ella.
Y el verso cae al alma como al pasto el rocío.

Qué importa que mi amor no pudiera guardarla.
La noche está estrellada y ella no está conmigo.

Eso es todo. A lo lejos alguien canta. A lo lejos.
Mi alma no se contenta con haberla perdido.

Como para acercarla mi mirada la busca.
Mi corazón la busca, y ella no está conmigo.

Poem 20

I can write the saddest lines this evening.

Write, for example: "It is a starry night,
and they shimmer blue, the stars, in the distance."

The night wind pirouettes in the sky and sings.

I can write the saddest lines this evening.
I loved her; there were times she loved me too.

On nights like this I had her in my arms.
I kissed her many times beneath the infinite sky.

She loved me; and there were times I loved her too.
How could I help loving her great, unwavering eyes.

I can write the saddest lines this evening.
To think that I don't have her. To feel that I've lost her.

To hear the immense night, more immense without her.
Each verse falls on my soul as dew falls on the grass.

What matter if my love could never hold her.
The night is filled with stars, and she is not with me.

That's all. Someone sings in the distance. The distance.
My soul is not content at having lost her.

As if to draw more closely, my gaze seeks her.
My heart seeks her, and she is not here with me.

La misma noche que hace blanquear los mismos árboles.
Nosotros, los de entonces, ya no somos los mismos.

Ya no la quiero, es cierto, pero cuánto la quise.
Mi voz buscaba el viento para tocar su oído.

De otro. Será de otro. Como antes de mis besos.
Su voz, su cuerpo claro. Sus ojos infinitos.

Ya no la quiero, es cierto, pero tal vez la quiero.
Es tan corto el amor, y es tan largo el olvido.

Porque en noches como ésta la tuve entre mis brazos,
mi alma no se contenta con haberla perdido.

Aunque éste sea el último dolor que ella me causa,
y éstos sean los últimos versos que yo le escribo.

The same night that whitens the same trees.
We, the two of that time, are no more the same.

I no longer love her, true, but how much I loved her.
My voice sought the breeze to touch her ear.

Another's. She's another's. As she was before my kisses.
Her voice. Her limpid body. Her infinite eyes.

I no longer love her, true, but perhaps I love her.
Love is such a fleeting thing, and forgetting is so lengthy.

Because on nights like this I had her in my arms,
my soul is not content at having lost her.

Though this be the last pain that she will cause me,
and these the last lines I ever write for her.

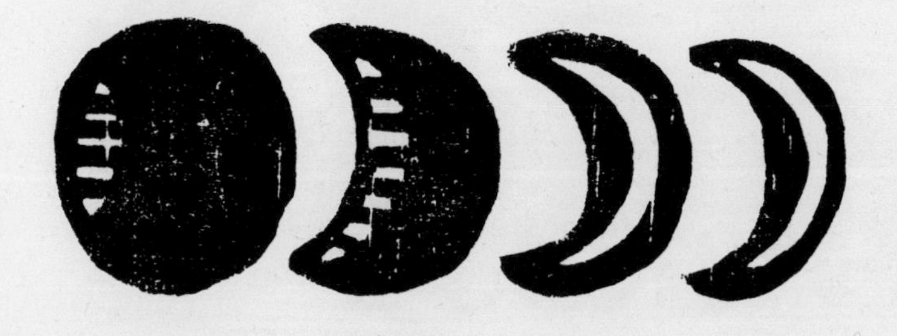

JUAN CUNHA

Uruguay (1910-   )

He was born in 1910 in Sauce de Illescas, Florida, Uruguay. When he was eighteen, he moved to Montevideo and shortly afterward published his first book, *El pájaro que vino de la noche* (1929), which was received by Zum Felde, the Uruguayan critic, as "the revelation of an authentic lyric temperament, uniting intense sensitivity to the strength of creative imagination, and both to a profound delicacy." In 1937 he published two books, *Guardián oscuro* and *Tres cuadernos de poesía,* after which he spent eight years without publishing. In 1945 he again commenced producing with regularity and in 1951 published one of the most important volumes of contemporary Uruguayan poetry: *Sueño y retorno de un campesino.*

Emir Rodríguez Monegal, another Uruguayan critic, has written of this book: "On returning to the world of childhood after more than twenty years of exile, on returning in dreams and not in reality, the poet Cunha finds a way of writing pastoral verse which has no parallel in our current poetry."

Following this fundamental work there appeared: *Variación de Rosamía* (1952), *Cancionero de pena y luna* (1953), *Triple tentativa* (1954), *Hombre entre luz y sombra* (1955), *Gestión terrestre* (1956-1959) and *A eso de la tarde* (1961). The sonnets which form the central part of this last book reach the height of Cunha's best work and demonstrate his enormous mastery of verse.

Paisaje

Pasó un caballo de estreno,
con una nube en el cuello.

Y una vaca, con un cuerno
de fiesta; el otro, de duelo.

Pasó una oveja, dos, tres;
más allá, fumaba un tren.

Deletreaba un burro un verso
mío. Venía de lejos.

Al fondo, un prado pedía
sus calzas, y su camisa.

Arriba, un cielo de lona.
No se enteraba gran cosa.

Y yo, o el viento, al final,
marcábamos el compás.

(El viento, o no sé si yo,
soplamos. Y se acabó.)

Landscape

A show horse came prancing by
with a cloud about its neck.

A cow with one happy horn
and the other in mourning.

A ewe passed by, two, then three;
beyond them a train puffed smoke.

A donkey traced my verses.
He had come from far away.

In the background, a meadow
asked for its trousers and shirt.

Up above, a canvas sky.
It wasn't noticing much.

And I, or the wind, at last
started marking the rhythm.

(The wind, perhaps I myself,
whistled a little. That's all.)

OCTAVIO PAZ

Mexico (1914-   )

Born in 1914 in Mixcoac, Mexico, Paz was a scholarship student in the United States and visited Spain during the Civil War. He was a member of the *Taller* literary magazine group. He has been in the diplomatic service for a number of years. His work has been translated into various languages. In 1963 he received the International Prize for Poetry in the sixth competition of the International Congress of Poetry, previously awarded to Ungaretti, Saint-John Perse, and Jorge Guillén.

Paz is probably the most outstanding present-day Mexican poet. Nevertheless, for a certain period his obvious dominion of language and verse paradoxically represented for Paz a limitation, as though an excess of intellectual rigor prevented him at times from reaching the true inner recesses of his themes. In his more recent books, to the degree that his language tends to become more stark and austere, his metaphors find their legitimate depth. *Piedra de sol* is not only Paz's best poem but also one of the recognizable peaks of contemporary Latin-American poetry. "With the exception of T. S. Eliot," the British critic, J. M. Cohen, has written, "Octavio Paz is the only contemporary poet capable of feeling his metaphysics and transmuting it into something alive."

His poetic works are: *Luna silvestre,* 1933; *¡No pasarán!,* 1936; *Raíz del hombre,* 1937; *Bajo tu clara sombra,* 1937; *Entre la piedra y la flor,* 1941; *A la orilla del mundo,* 1942; *Libertad bajo palabra,* 1949; *¿Aguila o sol?,* 1951; *Piedra de sol,* 1957; *La estación violenta,* 1958; *Salamandra,* 1962.

Nocturno

La noche de ojos de caballo que tiemblan en la noche,
la noche de ojos de agua en el campo dormido,
está en tus ojos de caballo que tiembla,
está en tus ojos de agua secreta.

Ojos de agua de sombra,
ojos de agua de pozo,
ojos de agua de sueño.

El silencio y la soledad,
como dos pequeños animales a quienes guía la luna,
beben en esas aguas,
beben en esos ojos.

Si abres los ojos,
se abre la noche de puertas de musgo,
se abre el reino secreto del agua
que mana del centro de la noche.

Y si los cierras,
un río, una corriente dulce y silenciosa,
te inunda por dentro, avanza, te hace oscura:
la noche moja riberas en tu alma.

Nocturne

The night of horse's eyes that tremble in the night,
the night with eyes of springs in sleeping countryside,
is in your horse's eyes that tremble,
is in your eyes of secret springs.

Spring eyes of shadow water,
spring eyes of cistern water,
spring eyes of dreaming water.

Silence and solitude,
like two small animals guided by the moon,
drink from those waters,
drink from those eyes.

If you open your eyes,
night opens mossy doors
on the secret kingdom of waters
that spring from the center of night.

And if you close them,
a river, a sweet, silent current,
inundates you within, rising, darkening you:
night wets the margins of your soul.

NICANOR PARRA

Chile (1914-   )

He was born in Chillán, Chile, in 1914. He is a professor of mathematics and is known as the founder of anti-poetry. He has been translated into various languages. Parra's conception of the anti-poem derives from a singular view of poetry. It would be too easy to say that the anti-poem represents a sort of literary atheism, a negation of poetry that serves in the final instance to demonstrate its existence. Nevertheless, the negation of poetry lies in the world the poet sees, not in the poet's gaze. Parra invented the anti-poem to scourge the world with its own whips, to battle with it on its own terrain. His attitude is opposite to that of the decadent poet, since the virus of decadence lies not in Parra's implacable and committed custom of contemplation but rather in the spectacle he contemplates.

Parra himself has defined anti-poetry as "a wrestling match with the elements; the anti-poet concedes himself the right to say everything without caring about the possible practical consequences which his theoretic formulations may bring upon him. The result: the anti-poet is declared *persona non grata.*" In one of his most recent books, *Versos de salón,* he displays a self-control that justifies the title and that permits him to utter the most iconoclastic and lucid incivilities in an impeccable manner which is mockingly respectful of the conventions. He has, in reality, dug his trench in the drawing room.

His poetic works are: *Cancionero sin nombre,* 1937; *Poemas y antipoemas,* 1954; *La cueca larga,* 1957; *Versos de salón,* 1962.

Oda a unas palomas

Qué divertidas son
Estas palomas que se burlan de todo,
Con sus pequeñas plumas de colores
Y sus enormes vientres redondos.
Pasan del comedor a la cocina
Como hojas que dispersa el otoño
Y en el jardín se instalan a comer
Moscas, de todo un poco.
Picotean las piedras amarillas
O se paran en el lomo del toro:
Más ridículas son que una escopeta
O que una rosa llena de piojos.
Sus estudiados vuelos, sin embargo,
Hipnotizan a mancos y cojos
Que creen ver en ellas
La explicación de este mundo y el otro.
Aunque no hay que confiarse porque tienen
El olfato del zorro,
La inteligencia fría del reptil
Y la experiencia larga del loro.
Más hipócritas son que el profesor
Y que el abad que se cae de gordo.
Pero al menor descuido se abalanzan
Como bomberos locos,
Entran por la ventana al edificio
Y se coronan con un nimbo de lodo.

A ver si alguna vez
Nos agrupamos realmente todos
Y nos ponemos firmes
Como gallina que defiende sus pollos.

Ode to Some Pigeons

How amusing they are,
these pigeons that mock everything,
with their little colored feathers
and their enormous round bellies.
They fly from dining room to kitchen
like whirling autumn leaves
and settle in the garden to eat
flies, a little bit of everything.
They peck at yellow stones
or land on the backs of bulls.
They're more ridiculous than a shotgun
or a rose crawling with aphids.
Their calculated flights, however,
hypnotize amputees and cripples,
who believe they see in them
the explanation of this world and the other.
But you can't really trust them, because
they have the fox's sense of smell,
the reptile's cold intellect,
and the parrot's long experience.
They're more hypocritical than a professor
or a fat, greasy abbot.
But at the slightest carelessness
they hurl themselves like mad bombers
through the windows into the building
and crown each other with halos of muck.

I wonder if some day
we will all really band together
and take as firm a stand
as a hen defending her chicks.

JOAQUIN PASOS

Nicaragua (1915-1947)

He was born in Granada, Nicaragua, in 1915 and died in Managua in 1947 without having published a single book. In 1946 he had prepared a selection of his work, but he died soon after completing the manuscript. This notable Nicaraguan poet, undoubtedly the most talented of the *Vanguardia* review group, is still today, more than twenty years after his death, scarcely known in Latin America. As is the case of nearly all the poets of his group and of the generation that followed them, Pasos is nationalistic, anti-Yankee and Catholic, but it is undoubtedly his dynamic, almost irreverent, religiosity that gives sense and cohesion to his voracious testimony to nature, to his turbulent political rebellion, to his urgent transits through love.

His compatriot, Martinez Rivas, has thus defined Joaquín Pasos' poetical workmanship: "To make a poem was to plan a perfect crime." In that sense, all of Pasos' poetry seems to have been planned as an incitement to his final poem, *Canto de guerra de las cosas* (The War Chant of the Things). It is said that Pasos came to define his own poem as "the human pain caused by the complaint of things." With an almost scientific curiosity about detail and eyes wide open in perpetual vigilance, the poet shows, image by image, a process of destruction in the course of which man's possessions subjugate man himself.

Pasos' complete works were edited for the first time in Mexico in 1962 under the title, *Poemas de un joven*, with a prologue by Ernesto Cardenal, another Nicaraguan poet.

Elegía de la pájara

¡Oh loca y dulce pájara comedora de frutas,
devuélveme el vino verde de tu plumaje esquivo,
derrámalo en el aire emborrachado a gritos,
agítalo en mi alma con tu pico desnudo!
Que la diosa que surte los campos de aves nuevas
vierta sobre mi sangre este licor agreste,
que tu color circule a través de mi cuerpo
nido de locos pájaros ¡ay! pájaros muertos.
Pero la dulce luna, la que escucha los cantos
silenciosos de las aves sin lengua,
vea en mi corazón como en un pozo límpido
el cadáver de tu alma flotando como un pétalo.
Con tu mirada ciega y honda como un clavo
estás fijando el vértice de este momento triste,
mientras suena en el aire rumor de plumas secas
y las alas quebradas se desgajan con sueño.
Sube, pájara, sube a la postrera rama,
la que despide al mundo, el puerto de los cielos;
lanza tu carne loca florecida de plumas,
lanza tu carne dulce perfumada de frutas.
Hacia ti estas dos manos, estas manos que esperan
el manojo de sangre de selva de tu cuerpo
para mostrarlo al mundo como una joya fúlgida,
como lo mejor, lo mejor de la cosecha.
Sobre este llanto mío que se apague tu vuelo,
que se ahogue en sollozos el clarín de tu grito,
y que tu cuerpo tibio descanse para siempre
en mi dolor que tiene la forma de tu nido.

Elegy of the Bird

Oh, wild and sweet bird, devourer of fruits,
give me back the green wine of your shy plumage,
spill it out upon the shouting drunken air,
stir it into my soul with your naked beak.
May the goddess who seeds fields with young birds
pour over my blood this pastoral liquor
so your color circulates through my body,
through this nest of wild birds, ah! dead birds.
But the sweet moon, she who listens to the songs,
to the soundless songs of tongueless birds,
sees within my heart as in a limpid well
the corpse of your soul floating like a petal.
Your gaze, sightless and as deep as a nail,
holds fast the vertex of this painful moment,
while rustling dry feathers resound in the air
and the broken wings are torn away by sleep.
Rise, bird, rise to the ultimate branch
that bids the world farewell, port of the heavens;
launch your wild flesh, garlanded with feathers,
launch your untainted flesh, perfumed with fruits.
These two hands reach for you, these hands that await
the palmful of jungle blood in your body
to show the world like a resplendent jewel,
like the best, the very best of the harvest.
May these tears of mine extinguish your flight,
may your trumpet cry be smothered in my sobs,
and may your ardent body rest forever
in my sorrow which has the form of your nest.

IDEA VILARIÑO

Uruguay (1920-   )

Idea Vilariño was born in Montevideo, Uruguay, in 1920. She is a professor of literature. The appearance of Idea's first book, *La suplicante,* in 1945, was an extraordinary event in Uruguayan poetry, not only because of the freshness in rhythm and language that her work represented almost from its beginning, but also because of the desolate, sincere, pathetic vision of the world that, in well-minted verses, this new and implacable voice transmitted. She moves from transparent air to dirty air, from plenitude to abandonment, from beings who "gaze at each other with eternal gazes" to the other wretched being, "isolated/alone as a corpse in its double box."

How can life be enjoyed when it is seen as so fragile, so absurdly fragile, when it is like a fluttering postponement of death? To exorcise such fatality, this poetess finds herself more defenseless than others. She lacks belief in God. Nevertheless, she has an impulse, a forceful substitute: she wishes to testify to a dark vision, to her particular inferno, to her dive into conscience, to her legitimate and condemned aspiration for a distant, dim happiness. Possessed of a demanding, self-critical stance, Idea Vilariño has attempted to weed out of her poetry everything superfluous, every interchangeable word, all parasitic emotion. What is left is the essence of her tortures, of her nostalgias, of her stark frankness, of her most solitary solitude.

Her poetic works are: *La suplicante,* 1945; *Cielo cielo,* 1947; *Paraíso perdido,* 1949; *Por aire sucio,* 1951; *Nocturnos,* 1955; *Poemas de amor,* 1958; *Pobre mundo,* 1967.

Volver

Quisiera estar en casa
entre mis libros
mi aire mis paredes mis ventanas
mis alfombras raídas
mis cortinas caducas
comer en la mesita de bronce
oir mi radio
dormir entre mis sábanas.
Quisiera estar dormida entre la tierra
no dormida
estar muerta y sin palabras
no estar muerta
no estar
eso quisiera
más que llegar a casa.
Más que llegar a casa
y ver mi lámpara
y mi cama y mi silla
y mi ropero
con olor a mi ropa
y dormir bajo el peso conocido
de mis viejas frazadas.
Más que llegar a casa un día de éstos
y dormir en mi cama.

Return

I would rather be at home
among my books
my air my walls my windows
my raveled carpets
my worn-out curtains
eat at the small bronze table
listen to my radio
sleep between my sheets.
I would rather be asleep in the earth
not asleep
be dead and wordless
not merely be dead
but not be.
I would rather do that than come home.
Rather than come home
and see my floor lamp
and my bed and chair
my wardrobe
with the odor of my clothes
and sleep beneath the familiar weight
of my old blankets.
Rather than come home one of these days
and sleep in my bed.

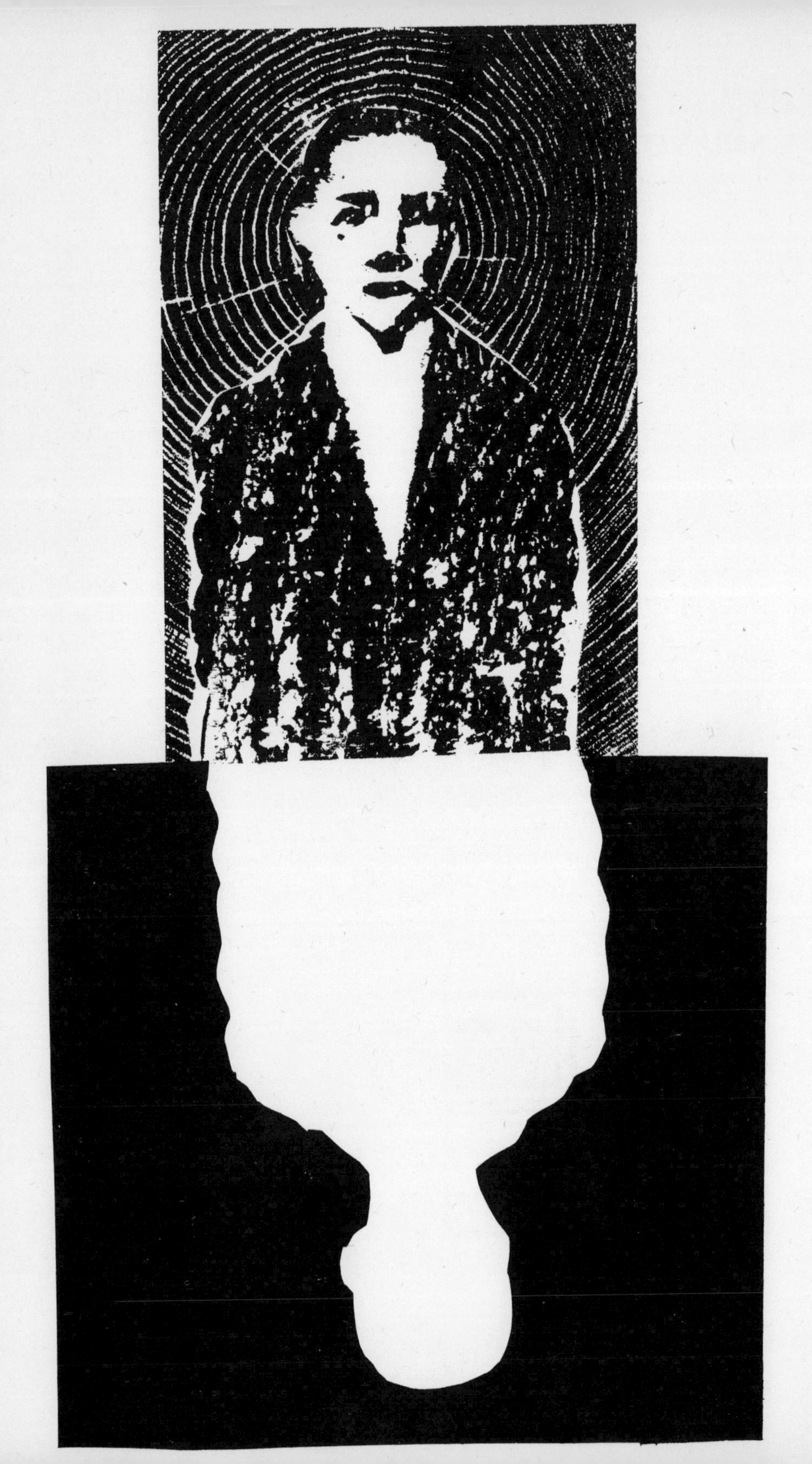

SEBASTIÁN SALAZAR BONDY

Peru (1924-1965)

Born in Lima, Peru, in 1924, he died in the same city in 1965. He was one of the most stimulating figures of the new Peruvian literature. A poet, essayist, short-story writer, critic, and dramatist, his work achieved a decisive resonance with *Lima la horrible* in 1964.

In Salazar Bondy's poetic work, there is always a recognizable attitude of nonconformity toward quintessential lyrics, toward pure and unlocated poetry, toward the ineffable. *Confidencia en alta voz* and *El tacto de la araña* are perhaps his best books of poems. In them, he does not bare his heart, nor does he offer his readers a wide-open door. The writer forms his confession from data, from indications, from the sort of experience that can be transmitted to another soul without running the risk of betraying one's self. Because of the originality of his focus, his patient sculping of the simple into high relief, and because of the human quality he always sets himself to capture, the present and future importance of Salazar Bondy's poetry is assured. The poem that is included here was written by Salazar Bondy only fifteen days before his death.

His poetic works are: *Voz desde la vigilia,* 1943; *Cuaderno de la persona oscura,* 1946; *Máscara del que duerme,* 1949; *Los ojos del pródigo* and *Confidencia en alta voz,* 1960; *El tacto de la araña* (published posthumously in 1966).

Testamento ológrafo

Dejo mi sombra,
una afilada aguja que hiere la calle
y con tristes ojos examina los muros,
las ventanas de reja donde hubo incapaces amores,
el cielo sin cielo de mi ciudad.

Dejo mis dedos espectrales
que recorrieron teclas, vientres, aguas, párpados de miel
y por los que descendió la escritura
como una virgen de alma deshilachada.

Dejo mi ovoide cabeza, mis patas de araña,
mi traje quemado por la ceniza de los presagios,
descolorido por el fuego del libro nocturno.

Dejo mis alas a medio batir, mi máquina
que como un pequeño caballo galopó año tras año
en busca de la fuente del orgullo donde la muerte muere.

Dejo varias libretas agusanadas por la pereza,
unas cuantas díscolas imágenes del mundo
y entre grandes relámpagos algún llanto
que tuve como un poco de sucio polvo en los dientes.

Acepta esto, recógelo en tu falda como unas migajas
da de comer al olvido con tan frágil manjar.

Holographic Testament

I leave my shadow,
a sharpened needle that wounds the street
and with sad eyes examines the walls,
the grated windows of inept loves,
the heavenless sky of my city.

I leave my spectral fingers
that skimmed keys, abdomens, waters, honeyed eyelids,
and through which writing descended
like a virgin's unraveling soul.

I leave my ovoid head, my spidery legs,
my suit scorched by ashes of foreboding,
discolored by the flame of nocturnal books.

I leave my wings at mid-beat, my typewriter
that galloped along the years like a small pony
in quest of the fount of pride where death dies.

I leave various notebooks, worm-eaten by sloth,
a few peevish images of the world,
and amid lightning crashes a sob
that stuck to my teeth like gritty dust.

Accept these; sweep them into your skirt like crumbs
and pacify forgetting with these small morsels.

CLARIBEL ALEGRÍA

El Salvador (1924-)

Born in Nicaragua in 1924, she considers herself Salvadorean, since from infancy she lived in Santa Ana, the second city of El Salvador. She is married to the North American writer, Darwin J. Flakoll. The two are joint authors of *New Voices of Hispanic America,* an anthology of Latin-American poems and short stories published in the United States in 1962, and of *Cenizas de Izalco,* a novel that was a finalist in the Seix Barral competition, Barcelona, Spain, in 1964. They lived in different Latin-American countries for a number of years and presently reside in Mallorca, Spain.

Claribel Alegría has published six volumes of poetry. In her fourth book, *Acuario,* 1955, the reader may discern the presence of a living being, possessor of a sense of humor as well as a vigilant intelligence, who tends to convert her melancholy attempts at communication with the world into something like the reverse of melancholy. In her latest book, *Vía única,* 1965 (undoubtedly the high point of her production), her poetry gains in depth and conciseness, which is a way of saying that it has gained in truthfulness. It is a book that settles accounts: with her roots, with her environment, with her past, but most of all it settles accounts with her personal abyss. Because of these things, this book of decisions, of self-revelation, has an interior strength that was not as clearly perceptible in her previous books.

Her poetic works are: *Anillo de silencio,* 1948; *Suite,* 1951; *Vigilias,* 1953; *Acuario,* 1955; *Huésped de mi tiempo,* 1961; *Vía única,* 1965.

Aunque dure un instante

Ahora,
mientras el río de obsidiana
nos refleja,
quiero hablarte de amor,
de nuestro amor,
de los diversos hilos
de su trama,
del amor que se toca
y es herida
y que también es vuelo
y es vigilia.
Sin él,
el verde de las hojas
no tendría sentido,
ni el farol de la calle
iluminando el agua,
ni la imagen ondeante
de la iglesia.
Mi amor es la escudilla
en la que tú dejaste una moneda,
la moneda tañéndome que existo,
la trenza que forjan las palabras,
el vino,
el mar desde la mesa,
los malentendidos,
los días
en que nos damos cuenta
que ya no somos uno,
que estamos alejados
irremediablemente.

Though It Only Last an Instant

Now,
while the river of obsidian
reflects us,
let me talk to you of love,
of our love,
of the diverse threads
of its pattern,
of the love one touches
as a wound,
the love that is flight
and is insomnia.
Without it,
the green of the leaves
would have no meaning,
nor the street lamp
reflected in the water,
nor the wavering image
of the church.
My love is the tin cup
into which you tossed a coin,
the coin clinking that I am.
It's the tangled tress of words,
wine,
the sea from our table,
our misunderstandings,
the days
we realize
we are no longer one,
that we have veered apart
irremediably.

Ayer,
desde mi exilio,
inventé que llegabas.
Salí del hielo,
espanté pingüinos,
desplacé a las estrellas
acechando tu desembarco.
Quería ayudarte a plantar banderas,
celebrar de rodillas
el milagro.
Ahí quedé
con mis señales.
¿Te sorprende mi vértigo?
Estoy hablando de eso:
de la alegre punzada
de saber que sí,
que de pronto es verdad,
que no estoy sola,
que estamos juntos bajo el árbol
con mi mano en tu mano,
que nos refleja el río,
que ahora,
en este instante,
en este ahora,
aunque dure un instante,
estás conmigo.

Yesterday,
from my exile,
I invented your return.
I broke through the ice,
startling the penguins,
displacing the stars
to search for your arrival.
I wanted to help you plant banners,
wanted us to kneel
and celebrate the wonder.
There I stayed
with my signals.
Does my vertigo surprise you?
I am speaking of it:
of the joyful stab,
of knowing that yes,
that suddenly it's true,
that I am not alone,
that we're together beneath this tree,
my hand in your hand,
that the river reflects us,
that now,
in this instant,
in this now,
though it only last an instant,
you are with me.

ERNESTO CARDENAL

Nicaragua (1925-   )

This Nicaraguan poet, considered the youngest representative of the literary generation of 1940, was born in 1925 in Granada, the oldest city of his country. He studied in Nicaragua, Mexico, and the United States. He took part in the rebellion of April, 1954. In 1957 he entered the Trappist monastery of Our Lady of Gethsemane in Kentucky, where he was a novice under Thomas Merton. He was unable to conclude his novitiate for reasons of health, however, and was obliged to drop out of the order. He continued his priestly studies in the Benedictine monastery at Cuernavaca, Mexico, and his theological training at the Seminary of Cristo Sacerdote in La Ceja, Colombia. He was ordained in 1965.

In his first poems, Cardenal writes with a spontaneous lyricism and demonstrates a formidable mastery of verse, as well as a singular aptitude for achieving a natural, communicative sound. *Hora O*, 1960, contains four poems written in Nicaragua during the period from the rebellion of April, 1954, to the assassination of Anastasio Somoza in September, 1956, which deal, without euphemisms, with revolutionary themes. These must figure among the most vigorous and effective political poems that have been written in Latin America. Curiously enough, *Hora O* is not a poem of hatred, but rather an X-ray of shame. Following the publication of two volumes of religious poetry (the voice, no doubt, of a poet within his retreat, but also the voice of someone who never tunes out the world even when trying to hear God), he published, in 1965, his *Oración por Marilyn Monroe y otros poemas*, a true poetic redoubt from which issue salvos of Cardenal's slashing and tender concept of human dignity.

His poetic works are: *Hora O*, 1960; *Gethsemani, Ky.*, 1960; *Epigramas*, 1961; *Salmos*, 1964; *Oración por Marilyn Monroe y otros poemas*, 1965.

Oración por Marilyn Monroe

Señor
recibe a esta muchacha conocida en toda la tierra con el nombre de Marilyn Monroe
aunque ese no era su verdadero nombre
(pero Tú conoces su verdadero nombre, el de la huerfanita violada a los 9 años
y la empleadita de tienda que a los 16 se había querido matar)
y que ahora se presenta ante Ti sin ningún maquillaje
sin su Agente de Prensa
sin fotógrafos y sin firmar autógrafos
sola como un astronauta frente a la noche espacial.
Ella soñó cuando niña que estaba desnuda en una iglesia (según cuenta el *Time*)
ante una multitud postrada, con la cabeza en el suelo
y tenía que caminar en puntillas para no pisar las cabezas.
Tú conoces nuestros sueños mejor que los psiquiatras.
Iglesia, casa, cueva, son la seguridad del seno materno
pero también algo más que eso . . .
Las cabezas son los admiradores, es claro
(la masa de cabezas en la oscuridad bajo el chorro de luz).
Pero el templo no son los estudios de la 20th Century-Fox.
El templo—de mármol y oro—es el templo de su cuerpo
en el que está el Hijo del Hombre con un látigo en la mano
expulsando a los mercaderes de la 20th Century-Fox
que hicieron de Tu casa de oración una cueva de ladrones.
Señor
en este mundo contaminado de pecados y radioactividad
Tú no culparás tan sólo a una empleadita de tienda
Que como toda empleadita de tienda soñó ser estrella de cine.
Y su sueño fue realidad (pero como la realidad del tecnicolor).

Prayer for Marilyn Monroe

Lord
receive this girl known in all the world by the name of
Marilyn Monroe
although that was not her true name
(but You know her true name, that of the orphan girl who
was raped when she was 9
and the shopgirl who at 16 wanted to commit suicide)
and who now appears before You wearing no makeup
without her Press Agent
without photographers and without signing autographs
as alone as an astronaut before the night of space.
She dreamt when she was a girl that she was naked in a church
(according to *Time* magazine)
before a prostrate multitude, their heads on the floor,
and she had to walk on tiptoe to avoid the heads.
You know our dreams better than the psychiatrists.
Church, house, cave, are the security of the maternal womb
but also something more than that . . .
The heads are her admirers, of course
(the mass of heads in the darkness beneath the stream of light).
But the temple is not a studio of 20th Century-Fox.
The temple—of marble and gold—is the temple of her body
in which the Son of Man with a whip in his hand
is driving out the money-changers of 20th Century-Fox
who made of Your house of prayer a den of thieves.

Lord
in this world contaminated by sins and radioactivity
you wouldn't only blame a shopgirl
who like all shopgirls dreamt of being a movie star.
And her dream became reality (but like the reality of
Technicolor).

Ella no hizo sino actuar según el script que le dimos
—el de nuestras propias vidas—Y era un script absurdo.
Perdónala Señor y perdónanos a nosotros
por nuestra 20th Century
por esta Colosal Super-Producción en la que todos hemos trabajado.
Ella tenía hambre de amor y le ofrecimos tranquilizantes,
para la tristeza de no ser santos
se le recomendó el Psiconálisis.
Recuerda Señor su creciente pavor a la cámara
y el odio al maquillaje—insistiendo en maquillarse en cada escena—
y cómo se fue haciendo mayor el horror
y mayor la impuntualidad a los estudios.

Como toda empleadita de tienda
soñó ser estrella de cine.
Y su vida fue irreal como un sueño que un psiquiatra interpreta y archiva.

Sus romances fueron un beso con los ojos cerrados
que cuando se abren los ojos
se descubre que fue bajo reflectores
y apagan los reflectores!
y desmontan las dos paredes del aposento (era un set cinematográfico)
mientras el Director se aleja con su libreta
porque la escena ya fue tomada.
O como un viaje en yate, un beso en Singapur, un baile en Río
la recepción en la mansión del Duque y la Duquesa de Windsor
vistos en la salita del apartamento miserable.

She did no more than act according to the script we gave her—
that of our own lives—and it was an absurd script.
Forgive her, Lord, and forgive us
for our 20th Century
for this Colossal Super-Production in which we all have
worked.
She hungered for love and we offered her tranquilizers;
for the sorrow of not being a saint she was advised to try
psychoanalysis.
Remember, Lord, her growing terror of the camera
and her hatred of makeup—insisting on applying her own
makeup for each scene—
and how her horror kept growing
and her lack of punctuality at the studios.

Like all shopgirls
she dreamed of being a movie star.
And her life was as unreal as a dream a psychiatrist interprets
and files.
Her romances were a kiss with closed eyes
and when the eyes open
one discovers it took place beneath reflectors
and they switch off the reflectors!
and they dismantle the two walls of the room (it was a
movie set)
while the Director goes off with his notebook
because the scene has been taken.
Or like a yachting trip, a kiss in Singapore, a dance in Rio,
the reception in the mansion of the Duke and Duchess of
Windsor
seen in the living room of the miserable apartment.

La película terminó sin el beso final.
La hallaron muerta en su cama con la mano en el teléfono.
Y los detectives no supieron a quién iba a llamar.
Fue
como alguien que ha marcado el número de la única voz amiga
y oye tan sólo la voz de un disco que le dice: WRONG NUMBER
O como alguien que herido por los gangsters
alarga la mano a un teléfono desconectado.

Señor
quienquiera que haya sido el que ella iba a llamar
y no llamó (y tal vez no era nadie
o era Alguien cuyo número no está en el Directorio de Los Angeles)
contesta Tú el teléfono!

The picture ended without the final kiss.
They found her dead in bed with her hand on the telephone.
And the detectives didn't know whom she was going to call.
It was
as if someone who has dialed the number of the only friendly
voice
hears only a recorded voice that says: WRONG NUMBER
Or like someone wounded by gangsters
who stretches out a hand toward a disconnected telephone.

Lord
whoever it may be that she was going to call
and didn't call (and perhaps it was no one,
or someone whose number is not in the Los Angeles directory)
You answer the telephone!

JAIME SABINES

Mexico (1925-   )

Born in Tuxtla Gutiérrez, Chiapas, Mexico, in 1925, he engaged in commercial activities and participated scantily in Mexican literary life. Publication of his first book, *Horal* (1950), marked the eruption in Mexican poetry of a colloquial style which was filled with surprises, rich in suggestiveness, and which achieved a spontaneous depth that was to become decisive (as an influence, as a bridge toward the reader) in the literary circles of his country. In the same year he published *La señal,* and not until six years later, *Tarumba,* whose poems offer an internal explosion of the sort that frequently occurs when the match of a sincere, unexchangeable anguish is applied to the long fuse of expressionist imagery.

Five years went by before Sabines published another book, *Diario semanario y poemas en prosa,* a slender booklet in which he alternates trivial notations with a compelling love-death symbolism. His most recent poems appeared, together with his previous work, in *Recuento de poemas* (1962). Although reluctant to publish in literary reviews, it was in *Pájaro Cascabel* that Sabines published one of his most admirable poems, "Algo sobre la muerte del Mayor Sabines," which ends with three memorable lines: "I placed beheaded angels at the foot of your box/ and I threw dirt, stones and tears over you/ so you won't get out, so you won't get out." Octavio Paz, another Mexican poet, has written: "Jaime Sabines installed himself from the beginning, without affectation, in chaos. Not because of love of disorder, but because of fidelity to his vision of reality," and he added: "His humor is a shower of blows, his laughter ends in a howl, his wrath is loving and his tenderness wrathful. He moves between the kindergarten and the operating table. For Sabines, every day is the first and last day of the world."

Los amorosos

Los amorosos callan.
El amor es el silencio más fino,
el más tembloroso, el más insoportable.
Los amorosos buscan,
los amorosos son los que abandonan,
son los que cambian, los que olvidan.
Su corazón les dice que nunca han de encontrar,
no encuentran, buscan.

Los amorosos andan como locos
porque están solos, solos, solos,
entregándose, dándose a cada rato,
llorando porque no salvan el amor.
Les preocupa el amor. Los amorosos
viven al día, no pueden hacer más, no saben.
Siempre se están yendo,
siempre, hacia alguna parte.
Esperan,
no esperan nada, pero esperan,
Saben que nunca han de encontrar.
El amor es la prórroga perpetua,
siempre el paso siguiente, el otro, el otro.
Los amorosos son los insaciables,
los que siempre—¡qué bueno!—han de estar solos.

Los amorosos son la hidra del cuento.
Tienen serpientes en lugar de brazos.
Las venas del cuello se les hinchan
también como serpientes para asfixiarlos.
Los amorosos no pueden dormir
porque si duermen se los comen los gusanos.
En la oscuridad abren los ojos
y les cae en ellos el espanto.

The Lovers

Lovers are quiet.
Love is the finest silence,
the most tremulous, the most unbearable.
Lovers are seekers,
lovers are those who renounce,
those who change, those who forget.
Their hearts tell them they can never find,
they never find, they seek.

Lovers walk around like maniacs
because they are so alone, alone, alone,
abandoning themselves, giving themselves each moment,
weeping because they cannot rescue their love.
Love preoccupies them. Lovers live
from day to day, they can do nothing else, they don't know.
They are always leaving,
always going off someplace.
They expect.
They expect nothing, but they expect.
They know they can never find.
Love is perpetual postponement,
always the next step, the next, the next.
Lovers are the insatiable ones,
the ones who always—how wonderful!—have to be alone.

Lovers are the hydra of the myth.
They have serpents where they should have arms.
The veins of their neck also grow swollen
like serpents to asphyxiate them.
Lovers can't sleep,
because if they sleep worms will eat them.
In the darkness they open their eyes
and horror falls into them.

Encuentran alacranes bajo la sábana
y su cama flota como sobre un lago.

Los amorosos son locos, sólo locos,
sin Dios y sin diablo.

Los amorosos salen de sus cuevas
temblorosos, hambrientos,
a cazar fantasmas.
Se ríen de las gentes que lo saben todo,
de las que aman a perpetuidad, verídicamente,
de las que creen en el amor como en una lámpara de inagotable
aceite.

Los amorosos juegan a coger el agua,
a tatuar el humo, a no irse.
Juegan el largo, el triste juego del amor.
Nadie ha de resignarse.
Dicen que nadie ha de resignarse
Los amorosos se avergüenzan de toda conformación.

Vacíos, pero vacíos de una a otra costilla,
la muerte les fermenta detrás de los ojos,
y ellos caminan, lloran hasta la madrugada
en que trenes y gallos se despiden dolorosamente.

Les llega a veces un olor a tierra recién nacida,
a mujeres que duermen con la mano en el sexo, complacidas
a arroyos de agua tierna y a cocinas.
Los amorosos se ponen a cantar entre labios
una canción no aprendida.
Y se van llorando, llorando
la hermosa vida.

They find scorpions between their sheets
and their beds float as if on a lake.

Lovers are crazy, only crazy,
without God and without the devil.

Lovers come out of their caves
trembling, hungering,
to pursue phantoms.
They laugh at people who know it all,
at those who love perpetually, faithfully,
at those who believe that love is a lamp of ever-flowing oil.

Lovers play at grasping the water,
at tattooing smoke, at not going away.
They play at the long, sad game of love.
Nobody has to resign himself.
They say nobody has to resign himself.
Lovers grow ashamed at all conformity.

Empty, but empty from rib to rib,
death ferments in them behind their eyes,
and they walk, they weep until daybreak
when trains and roosters sadly say farewell.

Sometimes there comes to them an odor of fresh-born earth,
of women who sleep shielding themselves with their hands,
contented,
of streams of fresh water and kitchens.
Lovers begin humming through closed lips
a song they haven't learned.
And they go weeping, weeping
for this lovely life.

JORGE ENRIQUE ADOUM

Ecuador (1926-)

He is Ecuadorian and was born in 1926. He has been director of the publishing house of the Casa de la Cultura Ecuatoriana, National Director of Culture, and Secretary of the Institute of Theatre and Folklore. When the military took power in Ecuador, Adoum chose exile. He lived for two years in China and presently resides in Paris. In his book, *Poesía del siglo XX,* he studied the work of a number of contemporary poets: Valéry, Rilke, Eliot, Langston Hughes, Maiakovsky, García Lorca, Guillén, Vallejo, Neruda, etc. A short collection of political poems, *Yo me fui por la tierra con tu nombre,* circulated clandestinely in Ecuador during the military dictatorship. His book, *Dios trajo la sombra* (the third volume of *Los cuadernos de la tierra*) won the poetry prize awarded annually by the Casa de las Americas, Havana, Cuba.

Adoum is presently the Ecuadorian poet who enjoys the greatest prestige within his country (Jorge Carrera Andrade, in contrast, is better known outside Ecuador) and is probably the only member of his generation who has influenced, not only by his work but also by his attitude, the younger generation. Adoum is a complete master of his poetic instrument, and his work reveals a rigor and self-discipline that not only does not obstruct, but also benefits the communication between poet and reader. It is frequently a committed, militant poetry, but it is the never-neglected artistic validity that in the last instance sanctions his political message.

Adoum's poetic work commences with *Ecuador amargo,* followed by *Notas del hijo pródigo* and *Relato del extranjero.* Nevertheless, the most important nucleus of his work to date is collected under the title, *Los cuadernos de la tierra,* consisting of four volumes: *Los orígenes, El enemigo y la mañana* (Ecuadorian National Prize for Poetry), *Dios trajo la sombra, and Eldorado y las ocupaciones nocturnas.*

Despedida y no

Como un muerto, amor, yo me incorporo,
echo puñales de olvido y grava, tablas
que mordí, piedras, lo que queda de mí
y de las flores que un día me pusieron,
y todo lo que echaron sobre ti para enterrarme:
las embriagueces de la equivocación, toda
la complicidad del amor, todo el amor
que confundí con el silencio, los clavos
que no me dejaban ir hasta tu frente.
Le devuelvo a tu ayer la herencia injusta
que me dejó en los ojos, mi desesperación
hecha de tierra, el llanto que sacaba
su alcòhol a las primeras cuerdas del pasillo,
mi angustia que presentía tu preñez, mis raíces
atadas a tu verdad enorme, tu alarido
en la espalda. Ahí quedan mi camastro
con sus sábanas de soledad y de melancolía,
mi empleo, mi patrón, mi desempleo,
mis deudas de aguardiente y aspirina, mis zapatos
llenos de no hay vacante y costuras,
los almuerzos en que me ponían un libro
abierto sobre el plato, mi espera de la gran
ocasión, de la gran cosa, del gran día.
Aquí comienzo, salgo del rencor como de madre,
me pongo todos los huesos. Yo me voy
de este hotel de pesadumbre a hoy día,
yo me voy a aprender la esperanza como una
lengua antigua que olvidé entre los escombros
de tanto ser caído en el fracaso, pero tengo
con quién hablar, con los que han muerto
por carta y no lo creo y llegan a enseñarme

Farewell and No

Like a dead man, love, I sit up,
scatter fistfuls of forgetting and gravel, planks
I had gnawed, stones, all that is left of me
and of the flowers they placed over me one day,
and everything they threw on top of you to bury me:
the drunken sprees of error, all
the complicity of love, all the love
that I confused with silence, the nails
that kept me from touching your forehead.
I give back to your yesterday the unjust inheritance
it left in my eyes, my desperation
modeled of earth, the tears that squeezed out
their alcohol on the first tiles of the hallway,
my anguish that foresaw your pregnancy, my roots
bound to your enormous truth, your shriek
in back of me. There stay my cot
with its sheets of solitude and melancholy,
my job, my boss, my joblessness,
my debts for liquor and aspirin, my shoes
replete with no help wanted and mending,
the lunches where they placed an open book
upon my plate, my waiting for the great
occasion, for the big deal, for the great day.
I start here, emerge from rancor as from the mother;
I dress in all my bones. I am leaving
this hotel of sorrow right now, today;
I am going to learn hopefulness like an
ancient tongue I had forgotten among the ruins
of so much falling into failure, but I have
people to talk to, with those who have died
by mail and I don't believe it, and they come to show me

su boleto, tu recibo hecho pedazos
por la crueldad del siglo y por las ráfagas
del año. Henos aquí, botín de tus edades,
hasta la altura a que has crecido, hasta
la línea del posterior rescate, prisionera
de ti. Almas amontonadas junto al muro,
caras contra la pared para verte por dentro
ese rostro de hermosa que estaba en las medallas,
y agarradas las manos a lápices, fusiles,
herramientas, cucharas: la batalla
es contigo y el regreso es contigo,
porque has de ser feliz aunque no quieras.

their tickets, your receipt torn to bits
by the century's cruelty and by the year's
gusts. Here we are, the booty of your ages,
as high as you have grown, as far as
the line of the last rescue, prisoner
of yourself. Souls heaped against the wall,
faces against the wall to see inside you,
that face of beauty that was on the medals,
and hands clutching pencils, rifles,
tools, spoons: the battle
is with yourself, the return with yourself,
because you have to be happy even if you don't want to.

CARLOS GERMÁN BELLI

Peru (1927-)

This Peruvian poet was born in 1927. To date he has published five very slender booklets: *Poemas,* 1958; *Dentro y fuera,* 1960; *¡Oh, hada cibernética!,* 1961; *El pie sobre el cuello,* 1964; and *Por el monte abajo,* 1966. José Miguel Oviedo, the Peruvian critic, has mentioned the "magical, nihilistic or ironic suggestiveness" of Belli's poetry. The trio of adjectives is particularly well chosen, since it registers a subtle interdependence of effects. In this author the combination of magic and nihilism is converted into irony; the proximity of nihilism and irony produces a magical effect; irony cuts through magic, and the result is nihilism in its pure state.

Social injustice hurts Belli, as it does so many Latin-American poets, but he carries this hurt to its ultimate consequences, to the point where he recognizes the total injustice of man's destiny. The poet anticipates the executioners and slices up the enslaved body; he records the illicit bruises; locks in metaphysical leg irons its limping hopes, its fertile idleness, its captive time. There are two of Belli's poems in which a phrase is repeated word for word: "that I see and abhor." This symbiosis (seeing and abhorring) characterizes a good part of the startling poetical attitude of this author, since in order to pour out the frustration induced by his sense of servitude, he has recourse to all his lucidity, which is considerable. It does not matter that this is expressed in baroque language, nor that it is subjected to the discipline of rhyme and rhythm; it does not matter, because this intellectual cargo functions as a display of human qualities and contributes to making injustice more visible.

Papá, Mamá

Papá, mamá,
para que yo, Pocho y Mario,
sigamos todo el tiempo en el linaje humano,
cuánto luchásteis vosotros
a pesar de los bajos salarios del Perú,
y tras de tanto tan sólo me digo:
"venid, muerte, para que yo abandone
este linaje humano
y nunca vuelva a él,
y de entre otros linajes escoja al fin
 una faz de risco,
 una faz de olmo,
 una faz de búho".

Papa, Mama

Papa, Mama,
in order that I, Pocho and Mario
might continue all this time in the human lineage,
how hard the two of you struggled
despite the low wages in Peru,
and after all that I only tell myself:
"Come, death, so I can abandon
this human lineage
and never return to it,
and from other lineages choose at last
    the face of a cliff,
    the face of an elm,
    the face of an owl."

ROBERTO FERNÁNDEZ RETAMAR

Cuba (1930-   )

Retamar was born in Havana, Cuba, in 1930. He studied literature in Havana, Paris, and London. He taught at Yale, was a diplomat in Paris, and served as secretary of the Union of Writers and Artists of Cuba. At present he is professor at the University of Havana, and he directs the excellent literary review published by Casa de las Américas in the Cuban capital. He is undoubtedly one of the most influential literary personalities in his country. He has published seven books of poetry (collected in a single volume, *Poesía reunida,* 1966) and three of essays.

In contrast to so many militant writers who select a message and advance toward it unconcerned as to whether or not their route of attack takes them through the realm of art, Fernández Retamar (a man who is singularly lucid and sensitive, spontaneous and a warm dispenser of friendship, ever disposed to recognize the lightning flash of humor in the midst of the storm) occasionally enters the political enclosure, but always with the full consciousness that in poetry the first commitment of all is to artistic validity. Fernández Retamar identifies himself as one of a sizable group in Cuba which was "caught between one class to which we did not belong, because we could not go to their schools nor come to believe in their gods . . . and another class in which we seek a place without having entirely its memories nor having entirely its same humiliations." He sees this group as called upon to serve a transitional function, to act as a somewhat shaky, hastily improvised bridge between two decisive instants of Cuban history. Amidst all the pessimists whose work overwhelms Latin-American printing presses, it is comforting to discover this excellent poet who is precisely the opposite: concerned and optimistic.

Niñas y niños, muchachas y muchachos

Niñas y niños, muchachas y muchachos,
seres prácticamente humanos y decentes:
agradezco de corazón la fineza
que los ha traído hasta aquí
con las uñas limpias, bien vestidos y peinados,
mirando de reojo mis libros
y mi calva indetenible.
Pero
no tengo nada que decirles:
soy lo mismo que ustedes, sólo que
han pasado los años, me han pasado los años,
y hay quien cree que así
uno está en mejor disposición
para decir algo.
Tengo malas noticias.
Yo también (hace quizás mucho tiempo)
me limpié las uñas, me peiné al lado, me vestí de limpio
y me senté frente a un calvo.
En vano.
Sépase pues:
no tengo nada que decirles.

Antes de separarnos:
buena suerte viviendo.

Girls and Boys, Young Ladies and Gentlemen

Girls and boys, young ladies and gentlemen,
beings virtually human and decent,
I am deeply grateful for the kindliness
which has brought you to this place
with clean fingernails, well dressed and combed,
glancing discreetly at my books
and at my invincible bald spot.
But,
I have nothing to say to you:
I am the same as you, except that
the years have gone by, the years have gone by me,
and there are some people who believe that
as a consequence one is in a better situation
to say something.
I have bad news.
I too (probably a very long time ago)
cleaned my nails, parted my hair to one side, dressed neatly
and sat down before a bald head.
In vain.
Know then:
I have nothing to say to you.

Before we take leave of each other:
good luck living.

JUAN GELMAN

Argentina (1930-)

Born in Buenos Aires, Argentina, in 1930, he is the most authentic creator of the young generation of Argentine poets and, in addition, enjoys the greatest prestige within and without the national frontier. He joined the *El pan duro* and *La rosa blindada* literary groups. Because of his leftist political militancy, he has spent long periods in jail.

Gelman's poetry reveals the visceral influence of Vallejo, but it is also an essential part of his experience as an Argentinian, as a man living in present-day Latin-American reality, which is full of conflict. His political message is assimilated into a poetic language of great expressive force, of good-humored imagination. His pessimism with respect to structures he considers outworn and his optimism toward a revolutionary modification he considers inevitable are coupled in a poetry that is strangely dialectic and profoundly original.

His poetic works are: *Violín y otras questiones*, 1956; *El juego en que andamos*, 1959; *Velorio del solo*, 1961; and *Gotán*, 1962.

La victoria

En un libro de versos salpicado
por el amor, por la tristeza, por el mundo,
mis hijos dibujaron señoras amarillas,
elefantes que avanzan sobre paraguas rojos,
pájaros detenidos al borde de una página,
invadieron la muerte,
el gran camello azul descansa sobre la palabra
ceniza,
una mejilla se desliza por la soledad de mis huesos,
el candor vence al desorden de la noche.

The Victory

In a book of verses spattered
with love, with sadness, with the world,
my children drew yellow ladies,
elephants trudging across red parasols,
birds imprisoned in the margin of a page,
they invaded death,
the large blue camel rests above ash-gray words,
a cheek glides across the solitude of my bones,
candor defeats the disorder of the night.

MARCO ANTONIO MONTES DE OCA

Mexico (1932-)

Born in 1932 in Mexico, he works as corrector of proofs at the University Press, prior to which he worked in a great number of other jobs. His poetic career began with *Ruina de la infame Babilonia* (1953), but was truly established with his fourth book, *Delante de la luz cantan los pájaros* (1959). In this same year he won the Xavier Villaurrutia prize. In 1961 he published *Cantos al sol que no se alcanza,* which is, for many, the best of the books this poet has written. It was followed by *Fundación del entusiasmo* (1963), *La parcela en el Edén* (1964), and *Vendimia del juglar* (1965).

"Only son of night,/ darkling mirage that leads me to commit serenities," is how he begins his poem, *Canción para celebrar lo que no muere,* and these two lines are quite representative of the habits and inventions of Montes de Oca. The influences of surrealism and of Vicente Huidobro, the Chilean poet, have frequently been detected in his poetry. It may be worth pointing out that Montes de Oca has less humor than is displayed by these predecessors, but in turn he makes a personal contribution that is not insignificant: his unusual metaphors like bubbles of words. The reader occasionally has the impression that if these bubbles touched each other, the entire poem would be destroyed. But fortunately they do not touch.

Atrás de la memoria

De hinojos en el vientre de mi madre
Yo no hacía otra cosa que rezar,
Por la grieta de su boca perfumada
Alguna vez el resplandor externo sorprendí;
No estaba yo al corriente de la realidad
Pero cuando ella sonreía
Un mediterráneo fuego se posaba
En el quebradizo travesaño de mis huesos.

Era el impredecible amanecer de mí mismo
Y en aquellas vísperas de gala y de miseria
Pude oír el eco del granizo
Tras la nerviosa ventana carnal;
Arrodillado estuve muchos meses,
Velando mis armas,
Contando los instantes, los rítmicos suspiros
Que me separaban de la noche polar.

Pronto empuñé la vida,
Con manos tan pequeñas
Que apenas rodeaban un huevo de paloma;
Jugué a torcer en mil sentidos,
Como un alambre de oro,
El rayo absorto que a otra existencia me lanzaba.

Cabellos y piernas con delicado estrépito
Saludaron el semáforo canicular.
Entonces halé hasta mis labios
La cobija de vapor que yo mismo despedía
Y me dormí en la profunda felicidad
Que uno siente cuando conoce el aire.

Behind Memory

On my knees in my mother's womb
I did nothing else but pray.
Through the fissure of her perfumed mouth
I glimpsed at times the outside light;
I had not caught up with reality,
But when she smiled
A Mediterranean fire alighted
On the fragile crossbars of my bones.

It was the unpredictable dawn of myself
And in those preludes of glory and of misery
I could hear the echo of hail
Behind the nervous window of flesh;
Many months I spent kneeling,
Keeping vigil over my arms,
Counting the instants, the rhythmic sighs
That separated me from polar night.

Soon I clutched at life
With hands so small
They could scarce enclose a pigeon's egg;
I played at twisting in a thousand ways,
Like golden wire,
The rapt flesh that hurled me into another existence.

My hair and legs with delicate clamor
Saluted the canicular semaphore.
Then I drew to my lips
The mantle of vapor that I myself gave off
And I slept with the profound happiness
One feels when he meets the air.